*"There'll he stand, looking across the bridge,
in the direction of his duty—and his destiny."*

THE GREAT VENTURE

By T. Morris Longstreth

IN SCARLET AND PLAIN CLOTHES

TWO RIVERS MEET IN CONCORD

HIDEOUT

THE GREAT VENTURE

THE
GREAT VENTURE

By T. Morris Longstreth

New York

THE MACMILLAN COMPANY

1948

Gratefully

to

MARGARET FRENCH CRESSON

whose

Journey Into Fame

suggested this book

Author's Note

This story of Daniel Chester French's life between his seventeenth and twenty-fifth years is based on the sculptor's diary and letters written by him and his family. Talks with his daughter, Margaret French Cresson, also a sculptor, and with others who have known him, supplement the documents. Mrs. Cresson has not only supplied invaluable data but has also very kindly read these pages to insure accuracy of fact and also of tone where Dan and his relatives have conversed.

Readers who wish to follow his career will find the full-length life of Daniel Chester French in a Harvard University Press publication entitled "Journey Into Fame," by Margaret French Cresson. This very fine biography traces the maturing of the sculptor's genius to its culmination in the great Lincoln of the Memorial at Washington. It is a kindling story, charmingly told, of a life that this nation will always be grateful for.

T. M. L.

Concord, Mass., 1948

O N THE morning after his seventeenth birthday, Dan French was driving his father to the Concord railroad station.

Dan was very conscious of his father's presence beside him, for last night's birthday party had brought a secret trouble of his to the surface, unexpectedly and embarrassingly.

Uncle Simon Brown and Aunt Ann were there and Uncle Simon had said to Judge French, "Henry, I suppose you've made arrangements for Dan's law."

"Dan thinks he doesn't want to be a lawyer, Simon," his father had replied amid a disturbing hush. Dan knew that this decision of his was a mortal disappointment to his father. His father's father had been Attorney General of New Hampshire. His mother's father, William Merchant Richardson, had been Chief Justice of New Hampshire. Judge French was an honored member of the Bar. Since Dan's brother Will was going into business, that left only him to continue in the great tradition.

To grizzled Simon Brown, Dan's refusal was too strange

to be borne silently. "Well, you're his father, Henry. He'll think differently if you tell him to."

"Now Simon," his wife interposed. "Times have changed. The War has upset everything."

Simon Brown twisted around to get a better view of this renegade. "What's the matter with the law, boy?"

Dan, for all his growth and manly voice, was a sensitive and rather shy youth. "Nothing, Uncle Simon. It just wouldn't suit me."

Dan's witty and able stepmother, Pamela, came to the rescue. "Dan isn't a bookish boy, Simon. And I must say I don't feel comfortable with those rows and rows of calf-bound tomes in Henry's office. Dan is going to surprise us one of these days."

"I don't care for surprises," Simon grumbled.

Aunt Ann, hoping to change the subject, said "Just what would you like to do, Dan?"

"You mean for a living?" asked Dan, groping for time.

"Yes, your lifework. Everybody has to have a lifework."

"I'm not sure, Aunt Ann," Dan confessed. "I don't know."

It made him feel like an outcast to admit it, but when he was asked to decide his future in a moment, his mind receded into a mist. He knew well enough what he didn't want to do. *That* list, topped by the law and going down through a multitude of professions and businesses, was as long as his arm. But he did want to support himself, although all he seemed to care about was to be outdoors, to work in gardens, or boat on the river, preferably with a girl. He was not lazy, but his gifts all pointed to one thing—that he was born to have a good time. But now, with the whole table listening, was hardly a good place to admit it.

Sallie's birthday cake, a four-decker with seventeen candles tracing his initials D.C.F.—saved him from more questions. Outraged, Uncle Simon was about to say that forsaking the law pointed to a serious mental condition, but he swallowed his words—and some cake.

After supper came the gifts; white boating flannels for the river from Pamela; a blue sweater, light as swansdown, knit by Sallie; ties from his sister Harriette in Washington; a knife and a book from his brother Will. His friend Will Brewster had sent him a book of rare birds. Aunt Ann gave him a copy of Mr. Emerson's essays, with the marker strategically placed at *Self-Reliance.*

Dan noticed that there was nothing labeled "With love from Father." Perhaps a wonderful new home, with a grand farm to enjoy, and an acre of garden all his own, was enough present for one year. But when the parlor was a sea of paper and the excitement spent, Judge French brought out a long narrow parcel.

"This seems to have been overlooked, sonny," he said in his dry way. "It's going to call down a lot of criticism on my head. In fact, I wouldn't give it to you if I didn't have confidence in your common sense and thoughtfulness for others. It isn't irony when I wish you may have many happy returns of this day."

It was a rifle—used, to be sure, but very little. No doubt it was one that had gone to the War over now for two years—and which the Judge had bought from a returned soldier. Some ammunition came with it.

Dan was almost silenced with joy, for ever since Will Brewster had been allowed a man-sized shot-gun, he had desperately wanted a rifle. And here he was being entrusted with a man-killer. Surely no one on earth had a kinder, more affectionate family—or one more fun-loving. The least he could do, he said to himself that night, was to turn out a shining hero. And he didn't mind working at it either, if only he knew where to begin.

All this made him conscious of his father beside him

3

while Stubtail plodded stationward along Sudbury Road. He wished to be grateful; he was grateful. But the trouble was that he had only made half a confession. He wasn't going to study law; far worse, he wasn't going to study. Not books. Not in a school-room. Never again. He wished he had got everything off his chest at once.

"Did you know what you were going to be at my age?" he asked his father defensively.

"I was brought up knowing it, son."

"I hate not to do what you want," Dan said. "But I wouldn't be any good at it. I know that. Sometimes I envy Patrick who never runs to a book when he wants to know something."

"A man in our walk of life has to have an education, sonny," Judge French said patiently. "If not for himself, then for his family."

"But he doesn't have to go to college to get it, does he?"

"I'm afraid he does, since he has to reckon competitively with all the other men who have gone to college."

"No college for me," Dan said with more abruptness than he meant.

Judge French was startled but kept his equanimity. "You will want to marry someday, won't you, Dan?"

"Certainly—any day now," Dan said with his quick smile.

"And have children?"

"Sure thing."

"You'll want to feed them heartily and dress them well and give them the advantages they see other children having?"

Dan saw where his father's logic was leading and had to acquiesce.

"Yet if you don't go to college, the most you can hope for is a day-laborer's wages, and you can't begin to support a

4

wife and children on that in the style you have just admitted is desirable."

These hard facts were unanswerable, Dan had to admit. But so were the facts of his nature. An ugly tussle loomed ahead.

Stubtail stopped beside the station platform and the Judge got down. He looked, with much unspoken sympathy, at his son. The boy, lean from his sudden ascent to nearly six feet, looked graver than he had ever seen him—an extraordinarily good-looking young man. No wonder the girls liked him. He had a handsome head and clean cut features. His dark brown eyes were singularly bright and alive. In this serious mood his sense-loving mouth had a new firmness and his chin was good.

"Don't worry, son," the Judge said as the train was heard. "We'll talk about it again. You're waiting for Will Brewster?"

"I might as well," Dan said. "He wrote he'd make the 7:48."

"Well, enjoy yourselves. I'll walk this evening so don't meet me. It's going to be a beautiful day."

It was, Dan thought, far too beautiful to waste in town. After five months of winter, the sun was joy enough without the birds and the trees budding and the new grass. He pitied his father having to leave the country for his city office to spend the day correcting stupid people and seeing to it that the law was conducted according to tradition. When he returned again on that grimy train, the day would be over. Half the year his father left in the dark and returned in the dark. It was as much slavery as the North had just fought so bitterly to abolish—more so, because his father had chosen it. His father loved the new farm and all that went on in the country. Then why did he give it up daily? So that his

5

wife and children should be brought up well and be as happy as other people.

Dan was perplexed. If grown people acted in such contradictory ways, they were hard to understand. His father loved farming. Why not be an out and out farmer, and trust that the happiness would come? Why not be yourself?

Dan was startled at the simplicity of the question. The sun came out warmly in his mind—for a moment. Then it went under the cloud again. What *was* himself? What did he want to be? A farmer?

In that lovely drowse of warmth it was hard to keep your mind on one thing. Dan turned his back on a girl who was driving up in a buggy beside an enviable young man. He determined to think this thing out. Of all the ambitions he had had, which was most desirable now?

At Amherst, where his father had been temporary president of the Massachusetts Agricultural College, Dan had been free as air after school hours to wander the hills and snare partridges. Then he had dreamed of going out West to hunt, living in the wilds as a trapper.

At Cambridge, he and Will Brewster had practically turned into birds. They hunted birds, stuffed birds, collected eggs and nests, and discussed ornithology as a career. It wasn't so attractive now, but it had knocked the bottom out of becoming a lawyer and turning to dust in an office.

At Exeter, New Hampshire, Dan remembered but one desire—to be out of doors. His first mother had died when he was six and Sallie, three years older, had been his mother, nurse, and friend. Flowers, animals, brooks—they were his life. Even now the enjoyment of outdoors seemed to sum up his permanent aim. But there didn't seem to be much money in it.

The train whistled and Dan, tying Stubtail to the weight from under the back-seat, strolled over to welcome Will

6

Brewster to Concord. Dan's walk had an easy-going gait that was American to the core. Although he was a new-comer to Concord, the three or four men he passed nodded or spoke to him. It was a friendly place, Concord. He liked it better than anywhere he had lived. Sallie said you were supposed to love your birthplace most, but she was probably thinking of cats, not humans.

That attractive girl was taking this train, Dan noticed.

He scanned the cars' steps. Will Brewster would be on the lowest one, leaning out. But Dan failed to see a long easy-jointed youth with a gun and his dog Jack trailing behind.

This was disappointing, but Will Brewster was not reliable in the spring. He had probably spied some tantalizing warbler on his way to the train and followed it. Dan knew exactly how he had felt, torn between his duty to be on that train and the something deeper in him that drew him to birds. Dan could visualize him following his instinct—and the bird, to the last feather and lisp of song, and then racing back to the station to catch the next train, sure of Dan's understanding. That was why they were such friends, because of this understanding. It worked both ways. While Will understood Dan's situation and backed him up, only Dan knew that Will wasn't going into his father's law office as he was expected to do.

Dan hunted up the station master as the train pulled out. "If you see a tall skinny fellow with a round face on top and carrying a gun, it'll be a friend of mine. Brewster's the name. Please point out Sudbury Road and tell him our place is ten minutes walk, on the right. He'll know it by the extra big barn."

The station master was very accommodating. Dan had yet to find a Concordian who wasn't, though he heard that there were some stiff customers in the town.

When he got back to Stubtail, there was Fanny Hubbard

7

sitting in his rig. She lived next door. She wasn't the prettiest girl in Concord but a very nice and pleasant one, and she could certainly make good gingerbread.

"If you're not going home, don't mind me," Fanny said.

"I'm going home—as slowly as we can get there."

Fanny's face lighted up when she talked with her new neighbor. "That suits me. It's so heavenly out."

"Did you walk in?"

"Cy has one horse and your Patrick is plowing with the other two."

Stubtail realized with happy surprise that he was already headed home, and he started to trot. Dan pulled him in short. "The idea! Hurrying like that when we've got good company!" he said to the horse.

Fanny laughed out of sheer contentment. "Oh, I'm so glad your father bought the place, Dan! We were afraid the Cutters wanted it, and Everett is the *homeliest* man!"

"It was love at first sight for all of us," Dan said, ignoring the implied compliment. "Mother Pamela wanted a smallish house. Father wanted lots of land and woods. I wanted the river and now we've got three-quarters of a mile of it. And Sallie wanted to be in the country but not too far from town and thinks where we are is just right. And when your father threw in the church pew and horse-shed, that clinched the deal. We had to take it."

Fanny giggled for the Frenches were not the steadiest of church attenders.

"I think it's wonderful what you're doing to the place, Dan."

"You've only seen the beginning," and Dan started to explain about the row of white pines his father was going to set out, the alterations and additions his mother wanted, and the casement window he was planning to cut in his room. Meanwhile Fanny wished it was ten miles to the farm.

8

It was so rare when she had Dan to herself. When he came over to their place her sister Susie hung about. When she went to visit Sallie, the place swarmed with girls, and they all felt the same way about Dan as she did. It was a wonder he wasn't hopelessly spoiled. Yet all the admiration ran off his back like water off a duck's. He never put on airs or traded on his popularity, and such quick popularity for Concord, if he only knew! The only provoking thing about him was that he treated everybody alike.

"I was thinking of making some molasses candy, Dan—if you'd like to come over," Fanny ventured.

"I've got to work—but I hope you make it," Dan smiled.

"It'll only take twenty minutes to throw it together," Fanny said. "And I need someone to pull it with."

Ordinarily he might have gone. Nothing he liked better than idling the hours away with a nice girl and lots of banter. But the talk with his father had sobered him. Either he had to discover for himself what he was going to work at, or accept his father's program for him.

Dan stopped Stubtail and let Fanny out. Then he turned and drove to the stable.

T HE NEW hired man, Patrick, was at the pump. "Faith, and it's come hot all of a sudden! Me face is tryin' to match me flannels."

His blue eyes and half of his sweaty forehead lapsed into the·shiny dipper. Dan watched his Adam's apple work up and down keeping time to his swallows.

"Where's your friend?" Patrick asked, reappearing.

"He'll be along. He's found some bird he liked better." Laughingly, Dan explained the nature and habits of an ornithologist in May.

"That's a provokin' kind of friend, ain't it?" Patrick asked. "It's lucky for him you're good-natured."

Dan, leading Stubtail to the trough, felt much the same way about Patrick. He was the highest type of Irish—handsome, intelligent, one who could never be thought of as a servant but as a person who chose to serve, and who happily combined an innate dignity with a sense of the ludicrous. He had simply turned up one evening and said he understood that Judge French needed a man. When asked for references, he said he didn't believe in them, but the Judge was at liberty to inquire of his wife. If he suited her he was likely to suit anybody.

Dan overheard his father chuckling as he told his wife, and Pamela said briskly that there was something to that statement. In the few months this wit and philosopher had worked on the place he had become part of it.

Patrick was now in the midst of plowing and Dan walked out to the field with him. He excused himself from cleaning out the henhouse or weeding the strawberry patch by reflecting that if Will had come he would not be working. And it wasn't every day that he could see horses plowing. There was something about horses he could watch for hours. He admired the way they moved, wondering if it was harder managing four legs than two. Their muscles curved under their skins like water over a submerged stone. Every rounding of neck and heaving side and shining rump had its special beauty. The total harmony of so many parts aroused a joyous interest in him. He wished he could see the muscles sliding, the tendons stretching and contracting.

Patrick's furrow was long and not as straight as possible, for it was a huge field. Like a dwarf, Patrick stood against the distant woods which the new leaves softened to a misty blue-green. The horses were coming towards Dan now, at once magnificently powerful and beneficently calm, much more impressive than Mr. Hubbard their owner. Dan was curious to find out how it felt to plow. Steering anything was fun—a sled, a sailing-canoe, a girl in a dance. How about steering these animals yoked to the plow! He would likely make a mess of it.

Patrick arrived, wheeled the pair, yanked the foot of the plow around, and leaned on the brace between the handles. Out came the bandanna. Dan squelched the fear of making a fool of himself and said, "Let me take her down?"

The hired man, who was four or five inches shorter than Dan, measured up the youth in his mind's eye. "Ye'll never learn. It's a man's job. Half way down the furrow ye'll feel like the pig who broke out and saw a cow and vowed if he ever got back to his sty alive, he'd never leave it."

Dan took the handles. "I've seen boys of fourteen plowing."

"It's not years make the man. Ye should know that," Patrick said. "The big thing is to keep the two horses abreast. These are gaited pretty even."

About to move, Dan was interrupted by two carpenters coming up to ask Patrick about a ladder. They did not move on at once and Dan wished he had kept his hands off the plow instead of getting involved in this exhibition. Patrick did not make it easier by saying, "The boy is out to show me how to drive a furrow."

"It was a ten acre field made a carpenter of me," said one of the men with a laugh.

"It's not so hard," said the other. "Just keep one eye on a tree, one on the horses, and one where you're walking, and you'll be all right, Dan."

"That's three eyes you've giv' him," Patrick put in. "The straightest furrow I ever seen was drove by a one-eyed man who had the sense to let the horses do it."

Dan grasped the worn wooden handles, held the reins as he had seen Patrick doing, and clucked to his team. They moved off in a stately calm. After an initial jerk, the steel share of the plow began tearing open the firm dark loam as easily as Dan shaved his cheek. The little gauge wheel that regulated the depth of the furrow was an unexpected help, and Dan had already picked out a tall locust tree as his guiding beacon. Fortunately this bottom land concealed no rocks. Taking a tip from Patrick's one-eyed man, Dan kept most of his attention on the tree. If you tried watching horses, the plow share, and your own precarious footing in the furrow, you'd be lost.

For half the distance down the field Dan was pleased with himself. He got deep whiffs of new-turned earth, heard the clank of harness chains and squeak of leather, paced himself to the plod of the heavy animals, and kept the plow handles from knocking the wind out of him at uneven places. But his muscles soon began to cry out at this unwonted use. Feeling as if he were being wrenched apart, Dan hoped he would not break an ankle stumbling blindly along the uneven footing.

Soon strain grew to pain, pain to anguish, and Dan felt that he must have plowed to Nebraska before he reached the end. He was sure he had sprained his wrists and ruptured his insides before he got the plow turned and the horses headed back.

This time he fixed his eyes on the blue-shirted Patrick. For some reason the distance seemed much shorter, and he had picked up a second wind somewhere. Aside from a cramp in one shoulder, he found the return not bad at all.

"You done good, Dan!" said one of the carpenters.

"Good!" cried the other. "That's the straightest furrow ever drove in Concord! Look at it."

Dan looked. It was indeed uncommonly straight, inexplicably straight, and he hadn't looked down at the plow once, except for what he could see out of the corner of his eye.

"When I was to the West," Patrick said, "I seen one line as straight as that. But then they was laying out a railroad."

Dan smiled and rubbed his shoulder. "Just the same, Patrick, I'd hate to do you out of a job." He handed over the reins.

The carpenters left and Dan walked to the acre of strawberries: his father gave him the income from this—on years

13

the blossoms weren't frosted. Weeding was a chore unless you had something diverting to think about. One thing, he did not mind being alone with his work. His brother Will was always talking about joining a firm, getting up a company, turning life into a hive.

As Dan removed the little weeds around the plants with long expert fingers, he considered this paradox. He was the most sociable creature. People found this out at once and were always calling on him to get up charades and tableaux and lead germans. When he went rowing he always wanted a girl in the stern.

Yet when he worked, like this, he did not mind being alone. He wanted to engineer the work, to do it his way, make it after his plan. Perhaps he was conceited, as Florence Gillson hinted—much to his inner wrath, for he knew he was not. He did not think he did things well and certainly was willing to admit that others did them better. Girls gave him a pain when they got to discussing conceit. If you had a mind of your own, you were conceited. If you believed in yourself, you were conceited.

Dan watched an earth worm coming out of the soil and forgot the weeds. What a life, to go shrugging along, carrying dirt! Yet they seemed to enjoy it. At least they didn't have to be educated. He lay down on his stomach so that he could see the now extricated worm ripple over the lumpy soil. A beautiful job. Dan wished he had a pencil but it was the motion that was beautiful and how could you draw that?

Gradually he became aware that he was being called. The shouting grew nearer, and Dan jumped up, knowing that here at last was his friend Will Brewster.

CHAPTER

3

D AN HAD never seen his friend so excited. Ordinarily Will Brewster talked confidently but slowly, as one who thinks things out for himself. Now he spilled out the news.

"There's a steer loose in Walden Pond woods. How far's that?"

"Only a little over a mile. How'd you know?"

"I overheard some men talking about it at the station just before Concord."

"Lincoln," Dan said.

"I was leaning out of the window and this man had come to the station to get help. He'd been driving some steers and one got away. A big black ornery animal. It broke away when he was passing these Walden woods. He said they'd never get it now unless they shot it."

"That's right," Dan said. "And I've got the rifle."

"You have?" Brewster was surprised.

"Birthday present from father. Look, I'll hitch up the horse and we'll drive over. Maybe we can join the hunt. Father'd feel he'd made a good investment if we brought home a hunk of steak."

Dan pushed Stubtail between the shafts and left his friend to finish hitching while he got his rifle. Will Brewster's father had long ago made marksmen of both boys with shotgun and rifle. To Dan this steer hunt seemed a providential occasion for his new rifle. He was not at all sure that Pamela would permit it. While his stepmother abstractedly agreed with the Judge that Dan was entitled to a gun, she was concretely opposed to his using one. And Dan was certain she would regard a steer hunt with a mob of men and boys shooting wildly at each other as the last thing in peril. Pamela rarely forbade him anything, but she would put her foot down flat on this one.

Quietly, Dan ducked in the back way and ran to his room, remembering ammunition and cleaner. He wondered if he dare ask for a lunch, but decided they could neither afford to arouse curiosity nor wait.

He had got to the head of the stairs when Sallie looked out of her room, looking like a duchess with a dustcloth about her auburn hair. "What're you in such a hurry about?" she asked.

"Will Brewster's come. I want to show him my rifle."

"He's got Stubtail out front. You're going somewhere."

Dan inwardly dratted his friend for exposing them but said, "We're going some place where we can shoot safely."

"Well don't go now, Dan. Dinner'll be ready in half an hour, and I'm going to make something that Will particularly likes."

"Can't it keep till supper?"

"No."

Dan lowered his voice. "Don't tell Mother Pamela this, but we're going to help a man find a steer. You'd do the same thing. If we're late, save some dinner for us, will you?"

The air of conspiracy won Sallie. They loved Pamela, admired her energy, envied her skill, and enjoyed her wit,

16

but after all they had been a unit before she joined the family and the appeal to a conspiracy, now wholly make-believe, still worked. Besides Sallie was unable to resist Dan when he showed he wanted something.

Dan drove with reasonable speed until they were out of sight and then persuaded Stubtail to lengthen out.

Will Brewster explained why he was late. It was not a new bird but a cat that had made him miss the train. A white-haired worried old woman had stopped him within a block of the station and asked him if he could tell her how to get her cat down from the roof. Dan laughed at the picture, for Brewster was the most obliging fellow. He was caught. When he had chased the cat almost to the end of the ridge-pole his train pulled into the station.

"But you never told her, I'll bet a horse," Dan said laughing.

"I almost did," Brewster said and Dan laughed harder than ever.

Still laughing the boys reached Walden Pond. It had changed in the twenty years since Henry Thoreau had kept solitary house there. Fires set by the railroad sparks had burned bald places in the woods. Yet there was cover enough to hide a morose steer effectually. And if he crossed the tracks he had the run of a wilderness that stretched unbroken to the Sudbury River and the wild hills beyond. There hemlocks and spruce and oaks sheltered the occasional lynx or the deer that found their way down from northern forests.

Dan found a small clearing by the road and tied Stubtail in a position so exposed that he could not be mistaken for a steer by the most excited hunter. Then he and his guest started into the wods. Dan decided to make for the sharp rise of ground on the Concord side of the Pond. The leaves were not advanced enough to hide what was going on, and

17

they could see or at least hear if a hunt had been organized.

As guest, Brewster was entitled to first shot. But as the rifle was a new gift Dan felt that propriety ruled otherwise and his friend agreed. So Brewster let Dan stalk ahead, just keeping him in sight.

For late April the sun was uncomfortably hot. Indeed, the whole season was weeks ahead of schedule. The birds shrieking to each other in avid delight made the woods sound like an aviary and Brewster, who would as soon have travelled without his pants as without field-glasses, forgot one chase to take up another. Or rather he stood still. Out of the welter of song his ear had caught a new note. There was the sound of three brown thrashers; from a thicket he made out the ringing song of a field sparrow; and some fox sparrows were rustling nearby. But what was that other sound? Some bird's young?

There was one way to find out. He kissed the back of his hand with a loud sucking noise that invariably made birds curious. Nothing was so curious as a bird, not even a thirteen year old girl. If this sound was from a woodpecker's nestlings it would be repeated from the same place. If it came from a full-grown bird, the sound would have moved in another direction.

He listened and heard a rifle bark. Not so far off, either. It must be Dan's. This was too much. Birds could wait.

Brewster loped through the brush, stumbling but unerringly arriving at the spot where Dan had been—at least the boot-prints were about Dan's size. Brewster listened but heard nothing. Perhaps he had pinked the steer and given chase. Brewster called.

"Over here," came Dan's voice from surprisingly near. It sounded weak and listless.

A quick fear chilled Brewster. "What's wrong?" he called as he pushed towards the voice.

18

No answer, and this alarmed Brewster still more. "Where are you?" he shouted.

"Here," almost from the other side of a great growth of juniper. Brewster found his way around and saw blood on the dead leaves. Now he was certain Dan had shot himself somehow. He parted some low little hemlocks and came out on a cleared spot. There knelt Dan beside a dying deer whose dark blood oozed from its mouth. Dan looked around and his face was all eyes, like a child's, and full of trouble.

"I didn't know it was a doe," Dan said quietly. "I guess I got excited."

"What a shot!" said Brewster, for the ball had evidently reached the most vital spot.

"Just accidental. I probably closed my eyes."

"Well, you downed her."

"Don't you see?" Dan said miserably, pointing to her belly. "She's got a fawn somewhere and still nursing it. Now it'll die too."

The deer's great eyes were glazing. Her hind leg kicked once in a last spasm; she raised her head, shivered, and then her muzzle slid back into its blood.

"That's enough for me," Dan said and he held out the rifle to Brewster. "You can go shoot the steer."

Will Brewster took the gun but the adventure had lost its zest. "What're you going to do?"

Dan was not sure. He felt a great shame and unwillingness to tell his father, to whom he told nearly everything. This careless wiping out of a life when he had just been entrusted with a weapon, affected him deeply. He felt sad and unclean. He wanted to be alone. Obviously Brewster had no idea how he felt.

"Will, would you do me a favor? Scout around over near those hemlocks. She was coming from that direction and her fawn may be over there. We could take it home."

19

Brewster left and Dan sat by the dead doe and gazed at the inert remnant of her beauty. At length it came to him what to do. When Brewster came back, reporting no sign of any fawn, Dan said, "I'm going to tell Patrick. He can use the meat, if it's good now. Is it?"

Brewster supposed it was, since the natives of Maine seemed to live on venison from one year's end to the next. He wanted to do something for Dan, whom he had never seen so disturbed. "I'll stay by the carcass while you're getting Patrick," he offered. "There are lots of birds."

"Thanks," Dan said. "Nobody is going to know this except Patrick and you and me."

Brewster nodded, and Dan, taking one last look at his handiwork, strode off in Stubtail's direction.

D AN WAS cutting asparagus—and thinking.
The trouble with asparagus was that you had to stand
on your head to cut it. Kneeling was too much of a nuisance;
sitting was out of the question. You waddled along the row
like an ostrich hunting a soft place to bury its head. Then,
too, there was so much of it—acres, for asparagus helped the
farm to pay. Worst of all, it was a perishable crop, forcing
you to rise at four, cut all morning and tie into bunches all
afternoon. Even when you were free to take Jeannie Richardson out on the river, you had to start home before you
had time to count the stars and it was ten or eleven before
you reached home. From then till four the next morning
time was so short it was hardly worth getting undressed for.

The trouble with thinking was its inconclusiveness. A
year and a month had gone by since the shooting of the doe,
and Dan had come to no decision as to his lifework.

He had not been idle. After a summer of considerable
usefulness on the farm and in the remodeling of the house,
with some studying on the rainy evenings when he could
not haunt the river, he had taken entrance exams for the

Massachusetts Institute of Technology—and passed. Since he had no sharply outlined wishes of his own, his sense of fairness made him accept those of his family. In fairness, too, he had studied, lugged books back and forth, pumped facts and theories into his mind and then pumped them out again on paper. Nothing in him kindled. He was allowed to stop. His real intelligence, he felt, had not been touched. The somebody that he was, that he felt had some unique purpose—and he felt this strongly in quickened moments—had not yet been called upon.

He had now passed his eighteenth birthday and was headed for nineteen: things were serious. He had got his growth. He was "as hilthy as the Tin Commandments" Patrick had remarked. He stood an inch taller than his father and alone had lifted a barrel of apples from the wagon to the cellar. All he lacked was an objective.

The need to answer the eternal question *What shall I be?* had been stimulated by words with Patrick. He and Patrick were cutting asparagus in opposite directions. When they met, they took time out to straighten their backs and relieve their minds.

On the last meeting Dan had said almost savagely, "I know what I'm going to be when I'm a man."

"What's that?"

"I'm going to be rich and famous and married to the three most beautiful girls in Concord."

"Faith, and you'll be busy!" Patrick said with a smile. "And whin do you expect to be a man?"

"I haven't fixed the date." Dan grinned.

"I thought as much," Patrick said soberly. "You're considerable past the day when I got me title."

"How so?"

"I felt me time had come and lit out from home. The day it don't set easy to eat another's vittles, that day you

22

become a man. And nought else has inything to do with it."

"How old were you?" Dan asked.

"Fourteen year, but I was near as big as I am now."

"And you didn't go back?"

"Back home? After comin' of age?" Patrick sounded surprised. "I did not. I got me a job as ship's boy on a three-master. And when it touched shore, I knew it was stiddy land that was me home and not that unholy fishpond. It's a great feelin', knowin' for sure where you belong."

This new insight into Patrick's sturdiness did not add to Dan's peace of mind. In the twelvemonth of deepening acquaintance with him, Dan had acquired much respect for his abilities. The man never boasted yet always seemed equal to his task, whether it was as farmer, woodchopper, ice-cutter, horse-doctor, harness-repairer, hayer, or purveyor of homely knowledge. And all this at thirty-five. All this on so few dollars a month that it made Dan uncomfortable when he tried to figure out how much *he* was worth.

When each cutter had turned and met again and stretched, Patrick said, "I've been thinkin' of this fix you're in, Dan. It reminds me of when I was to the West and run into a mighty smart woman out Kansas way. One day she was plasterin' and needed hair bad. So she up and shaved her dog and got it. See what I'm drivin' at?"

"Not exactly," Dan said.

"Well, she didn't worry about what someone else would do, she did what come to her to do. And if I was you, I'd do the same thing. I'd quit worryin' and let your work come to you, like it comes to everything in nature."

"How can you be sure it will come?" Dan asked.

"Look at them radishes yonder," Patrick said. "All they do's set and grow and their bite comes to them. And the same with humans. What's in you's bound to come out, if you'll let it."

"The family's complaint is that I do just that," Dan smiled.

"Yes, but you keep messin' around in your head, worryin'. Nothin'll come to you that way. You try nature's way and see."

"Meanwhile father's supporting me."

"You're doin' a good job for him, aren't you? Now you mind what I say and don't let anybody hustle you."

Dan resumed cutting with something new to think about. When the Meeting-house clock struck twelve he carried his baskets of thick healthy stalks to the barn and was free—free for an hour. Freedom! That was it. That was the goal. But how did you make a career of being free?

In the lofty barn with its end doors open to let the breeze through, the afternoon wore along.

This day there were only four of them—Pamela, Sallie, Dan, and Patrick. Dan's stepmother was a strikingly beautiful woman, slightly plump, with a brilliant complexion, white skin, pink cheeks, flashing black eyes, and jet black hair which she parted in the middle. Even now when her clothes were strictly utilitarian, she was charmingly dressed.

Slicing off the white part, Patrick laid the asparagus stalks with their heads all facing in one direction. Next Sallie inspected the stalks, and after throwing away the defective ones, divided them into lots. Pamela and Dan tied these lots into bunches, a job not so easy as it looked for the separate stalks were slippery and had to be bound tight without injury. From time to time Patrick removed the rapidly accumulating bunches and stowed them in crates for the market.

Patrick knew his place and let Pamela talk and Sallie gossip. But when the conversation lagged, he usually stimulated it by some tale or other that threw them all in stitches. This afternoon the heat was overpowering and Patrick full of reminiscences. Concord was not often bothered by tramps, but Patrick spoke of one who had come at dinner time to the French's kitchen.

"I hope you gave him something, m'am," Patrick said, rather to Pamela's surprise.

"I did, of course. But I think it is very weak of me," Pamela said. "It's easier than making them work for it."

"Why did you want mother to give him anything?" Sallie asked.

"When I was to the West I heard of a somewhat similar situation," Patrick said. "A tramp come to this lady's house and asked for food and she told him she had none.

"Well, he was a very sympathetic man, that tramp. He couldn't git her troubles out of his head. So he did the best he could. He went to each house he came to for five mile down the road, and told them that their neighbor was starvin' to death without a crumb of food in the house. It took the poor woman the most of a week returnin' the provision she found piled high on her porch by her lovin' neighbors. It was that kind of trouble I was hopin' you might be spared, m'am."

"Oh, Patrick!" cried Pamela, laughing so that she could not tie the stalks in her hand. "I suspect you were that wicked tramp."

"Why, m'am! I never went unfed onct, from Chicagy to Montana. I was put to it though, I must say, the summer I run into grasshopper country."

"Where's that?" Sallie asked.

"It's never the same place twict, you can bet on that," Patrick said emphatically. "They don't even leave the fences, those pests. Why out in South Dakoty, the jumpers are in the habit of gatherin' around the railroad station to see who comes to buy seed wheat."

"How could you tear yourself away from such a delightful region!" Pamela exclaimed.

"Well, m'am, I couldn't but for gettin' lonesome. Out there it only takes two men and a dog to call a town a city, and there weren't enough girls to go round."

"I know what you mean," Dan said, and they laughed.

"You didn't know Mary then?" Sallie asked.

"No I didn't, but I missed her just the same."

The clock struck five and Patrick went off to call the cows and see to the milking.

"I never cease to be grateful for that man!" Pamela said. "The evening he knocked on our door was a lucky one for the Frenches. I'm only afraid he'll get restless again."

"He's too fond of Mary and the children," Sallie said.

"A man can't drag *five* anchors!" Dan remarked. They laughed and Dan went on, "Patrick was telling me what to do about my lifework."

"What's he think you ought to do?" Sallie asked.

"Let it come to me. He says everything else comes to a man naturally. I mean he gets born and grows up without planning it all out, so why shouldn't the thing he's meant to do appear at the right time?"

"Do you think you simply grew?" Pamela asked. "You were planned for from the very moment that your father and mother were aware that you existed. You've been fed and clothed and taught this and that by looking ahead. Now we think it's time that you took over the planning. I doubt if careers come by spontaneous combustion."

"That's not quite the point," Dan said. "You and father have given me the food. But who gave me the hunger? Why, nature. And what's a career but the satisfaction of another hunger? So why shouldn't I rely on nature to give me that hunger too?"

Sallie looked with pride at her baby brother.

26

Pamela was not impressed. "It simply doesn't work out that way. You can't sit around forever waiting for some ambition to spring up in you. You have to decide what your ambition is and then cultivate it the best you can."

"But it has to be *my* ambition, doesn't it?" Dan asked and a seriousness that neither Sallie nor Pamela had heard before was in his voice.

"Certainly. Neither your father nor anyone else is trying to impose an ambition on you. But you've declined to go to college and fit yourself for a profession. You say you have no interest in business. You doubt now that you want to take up farming. You have too much promise to do nothing, even if we could afford to support you."

"Patrick left home at fourteen," Dan said. "There may be something in it."

"No! No!" Sallie jumped up and put her arms about her brother's neck. "Harriette's gone to New Hampshire and Will's going to Chicago and I don't intend to lose you!"

Pamela rose and smoothed her skirt. "We're all tired," she said. "I understand what you're driving at, Dan. I expect that's the way geniuses start. They feel an urge so strong that it drives them to play the organ, as Mozart did at six, or write poetry, like Keats. But ordinary people like the rest of us have to find out what we can do best and then put our minds to it and do it."

She rested her hands on Dan's shoulders, for he was still sitting down, and kissed the tip of one ear. "You are going to be generous all your life, your ears are so big." Then to Sallie, "Do you think Ned Bartlett is coming to supper?"

Sallie was sure he intended coming and the two women hurried off to prepare, knowing Dan would tie up the last few stalks. The afternoon left him deeply disturbed. He liked Patrick's idea of your lifework blossoming out of you as naturally and logically as an apple tree put forth its blos-

27

soms in the spring. He had hoped Pamela would see how true it ought to be. He might have known, though, that she wouldn't. Women were always doing something practical—making beds, sweeping, baking bread, or as in Mary's case, producing babies and making clothes. Women never sat around cracker-barrels in stores discussing politics and horse-races. If they talked, they knit. They liked to see the effect taking place before their eyes. You couldn't imagine a woman going off into the woods, the way they said Thoreau used to do, to brood over the laws of the universe.

Dan laughed aloud at the picture of Pamela sitting on a fence-rail brooding. She would have thought of a dozen things that had to be done and hopped down to set about doing them. Probably she thought him lazy as a sponge proposing to await a divine selection of his lifework. Yet, when the whole force of what you called yourself cried out the rightness of such a proposal, you had to pay it some heed.

He cut the last string, placed the new-made bunches with the others, and stooped to throw a fallen turnip into the dustbin. Its forked root and bulging white belly for some reason suggested an animal. Dan smiled. Given eyes and a mouth and a little shaping off, it could easily be a frog. He reached for his knife.

It was refreshing to sit down in the big doorway facing the quiet of the orchard while he cut away bits of the turnip with his knife. The more he carved the more likely the frog became. Jeannie would be amused by it. He would finish it up into a real frog and surprise her. Jeannie was vastly appreciative—a tail-coat and trousers would turn it into the Frog-who-would-a-wooing-go.

Now he was working in earnest. The afternoon's fatigue was forgotten, and with it went all the disappointment at Pamela's viewpoint. With every careful stroke of his knife, the joviality and lifelikeness of the frog emerged. By Harry!

28

He was a regular Lochinvar of a frog, even if he had come out of a turnip instead of the West. A paring here, a scrape there, and Dan grinned. The creature was gallant as all get out, ready to bow to the lady-frog of his choice, "Mr. French calling on Miss Richardson and hopes she will go for a swim."

Dimly, he heard a bell. Supper. Well, he couldn't stop now.

Twenty minutes later he went inside. Pamela heard him and called, "Hurry, Dan! Everything will be cold."

As he reached the door, Sallie said, "What in the world kept you?"

Dan greeted Ned Bartlett and his father and quietly placed the frog in front of Judge French. As he withdrew to wash, he heard Sallie's little scream of delight. More voices came to him on his way upstairs, voices of surprise and approval mingled with pleased laughter.

He paused on the top step to hear his father say, "Pamela, this really looks like talent."

ALL THE next day it rained and they had a day's rest
from asparagus. Dan spent the time painting the
woodwork of a room Pamela wanted done over. He was glad
to be alone. The releasing of the frog from that turnip had
aroused him. You saw something with your mind's eye, your
hands made that something visible, and you felt happy at
the achievement. Whenever his thought came back to what
he had done with that forked turnip he felt pleased beyond
all reason.

He hitched Stubtail and drove to meet his father at the
station. In spite of the rain the robins were putting the day
to bed with song. He felt good, too. He would take the frog
to Jeannie this evening. His family had been so pleased by
it that he had left it with them, but he had told Jeannie
about it and her eyes sparkled. Girls were really very satisfactory. They appreciated what you did much more easily
than any male friends.

The train stopped and Dan saw his father coming towards
him with that quick resilient step of a man who can abide
nothing tedious. He was carrying a package. Dan took it to

stow in the rear. "What's that?" he asked, for it was heavy.

"A new game," the Judge's light gray eyes shone.

"What game? Quoits?"

"It's a game I made up. Your frog gave me the idea. If I have one artist in the family, I may have half a dozen. So I bought some potter's clay and we'll have a competition after supper."

Dan was amused—and excited. All day he had been considering how to go about repeating that frog in some substance more lasting than a turnip. And now his father had answered his unspoken wish.

Supper provided the usual tilting match that kept their society bubbly and enterprising. Sallie was enthused about the doorstep party she was getting up to surprise Fanny Hubbard.

"What girls are you asking?" Dan inquired.

"Yours mostly," Sallie patted his brown hand. "All six of them."

"That's slander!" Dan's grin began. "Father, what are the libel laws? I want to sue."

"Do you consider that you have been injured by this defamatory statement?" asked the Judge and the others laughed.

"I'd be injured if the other five found out," Dan said. "Besides, I've never had six, not all at once."

Pamela stopped dishing the strawberries to say, "It might be better if you had, Dan. If you pay too much attention to one, she is bound to believe you are more interested in her than the others."

"Maybe I am," the grin widened.

"Then you are heading for trouble."

"I wish I knew how to suit everybody," Dan said good-humoredly. "If I call on one girl three nights in succession,

31

we're reported engaged. If I call on two, I'm put down as unfaithful. Three's worse. I'm nothing but a flirt. What shall I do, wear a placard around my neck *Intentions honorable but postponed for lack of cash?*"

Sallie's red head shook in laughter. "No, Dan, just go on being your sweet self and send the broken hearts to me."

"You flatter me," Dan remarked. "I wouldn't know a broken heart if I saw one."

"That is precisely the point," Pamela said energetically.

Judge French folded his napkin and pushed back from the table. "Dan knows what is right, Pamela. Now where do you want us to hold this sculpture competition?"

The kitchen, Pamela decided, was the best place to make a mess. They put on aprons and sat down around the big table, each with a lump of clay to do with as he wished—or was able.

For an hour they labored in comparative silence. This was Dan's first experience with clay and he was surprised to find how it obeyed every touch, harsh or gentle. Press it ever so slightly and it stayed pressed. Push it back again and it stayed back.

"Talk about libel!" Judge French said after a while. "This stuff mocks me. It misrepresents me and exposes me to ridicule."

"Isn't it hateful!" Pamela cried. "I thought I could at least do your profile, Henry, and look at it!" They looked.

"I call that successful!" the Judge said gallantly. "One sees that it has a nose."

Sallie gave up first. She had thought a horse might be practicable. It wasn't.

The Judge left his mound of clay and went over to Dan. Plodding along, Dan was nowhere near half done, but already the figure was emerging—a dog's head, recumbent between two paws. Everything was still in the rough, but the

32

proportions looked reasonable, and the ears, as Dan made them prick up and forward, had personality.

"That's Jack, isn't it?" Judge French asked.

"Trying to be," Dan murmured.

Jack was still Will Brewster's companion and shadow, the dog with six pedigrees and a heart of gold. As the long strong fingers continued working, Jack's smooth-haired nervous muzzle emerged. The hour hand moved from nine to ten. Sallie yawned and withdrew. Pamela said, "Please don't wear yourself out, Dan," and retired. Even the Judge at last left his son to finish alone.

He walked upstairs thoughtfully and said to his wife, "He's got it, Pamela. The gift's there."

Pamela looked at her husband from the pillow. "What are you going to do about it, Henry?"

"The same as I do with the asparagus, I reckon. Cultivate it a little and let it grow."

Downstairs the hour hand passed eleven and then twelve, and still the youth bent over the figure taking shape beneath his hands.

Dan, the unsecretive, now had a secret. To keep it, he had requested everyone to keep out of his room, knowing that in this household of mutual love and courtesy his request would be respected.

During the day he cut and tied asparagus. After supper he closeted himself in his chamber and the lamplight shone under the door until late at night. Pamela did not have to worry about his late hours on the river with a girl. There was no girl. There was no river.

When night followed night into the second week of this concentration, Pamela began to fret. It was not good for him to be shut up so long. The dog's head must be finished by now.

"We wanted him to get absorbed in something," the Judge reminded his wife.

"Yes, but what will the room look like?" Pamela demanded. "I left clean sheets at the door but I doubt if he has put them on the bed."

"I doubt it, too," Judge Henry smiled.

"You take things very lightly," Pamela said. "Tomorrow evening Sallie has her doorstep party and I simply have to have the room cleaned."

"I don't see why. The party is to be on the doorstep not in Dan's room."

"A man never would see!" Pamela exclaimed. "I can't feel comfortable with guests coming and a room as disreputable-looking as Dan's must be. Suppose someone should accidentally look in?"

"We will lock it," the Judge said. "I will carry this case to the Supreme Court if necessary."

"Donkey!" Pamela cried as she kissed her husband, but she much preferred to have her men stand up for their rights.

It was about ten that May morning when Dan straightened up from the asparagus patch. Unkinking his back, he saw smoke rising from behind the elms near the Badger place. There was so little smoke that he might have paid no attention to it if he had not been in need of diversion.

He continued looking and presently the smoke thickened. Henry Badger burning brush, no doubt. But why so close to the barn? A new puff, darker than before, startled him. It must be the barn itself. That was bad.

Dan ran to the barn and shouted for Patrick. No response. Then he remembered: Patrick was readying the river-field for planting corn. Dan took the water-buckets that were always filled and hung inside the door and ran to the house.

34

"Badger's barn's afire!" he shouted. Sallie's head appeared at a second-story window.

"Whose barn?"

"Henry Badger's it looks like."

"Oh, Dan! All those horses!"

"Will you tell Cy Hubbard and everybody! I'm going over."

"Danny! Be careful!" Sallie cried after him.

He jogged down the road with his half-filled buckets. There never were enough buckets at a fire, and the Concord Fire Company would be a long time coming.

The smoke was pillaring up now. Dan was no more immune to the excitement of a conflagration than other men, but he hated destruction. He hated others to suffer, and he felt especially sorry for the Badgers, who never had any luck.

Coming around the dusty curve he saw flames had broken through the roof at one corner. The draft thus caused made the fire roar. Fortunately there was no wind, but the drift of air carried sparks over the house.

Strangely there was no sign of life, only a little girl of eight or nine on the front step of the house, crying. "Where's your father, Emmy?" Dan asked.

"I don't know. . . . I don't know," sobbed the child.

Suddenly, carrying a picture of her father under one arm and a handful of silver in the other, Mrs. Badger came out of the house. She was beside herself with fright. "Oh, Mr. Dan!" she cried. "Henry's to the village, and Larry's gone to save the horses, and I'm terrible afraid he'll be smothered."

"We've several minutes yet," Dan said. "I'll help him." He set the buckets down as Mrs. Wheeler came running from her house. No Cy in sight, though. Nobody. But the fire couldn't have been going ten minutes.

Dan started towards the stable at the end of the barn and

35

almost crashed into Patrick coming around the corncrib. His face was red as the flames from running.

"Mr. Badger's away and Larry's trying to get out the horses," Dan explained. "We tie bags over their eyes, don't we?"

Patrick glanced at the roof of the dwelling. "You run up and climb out the trap and stop those shingles from catching," he said between gasps for breath. "I'll tend to the horses. There's but four."

Dan knew that Patrick was trying to shield him. "Time enough for that," he said. "I'm helping you."

He felt Patrick's hand rough on his shoulder. The roar had increased. Half the roof was gone. "Save the house, I tell you."

"Here comes Cy," Dan said and shook himself loose from Patrick.

It was already smoky in the stable. Above the fire, Dan heard the commotion of horses stomping, and above that the voice of fifteen-year-old Larry shouting "Come on, come on, Prince. Come *on,* you brute." The horse did not budge as the lurid light coming in through the windows grew more terrifying.

Patrick pushed Larry away. "Get me a potato sack," he shouted. "Get several. Or anything that'll cover their eyes—quick!"

Dan picked up a saddle blanket and went into the next stall. The horse was in a paralysis of fright, and Dan had to fight to keep his own nervousness down. The roar was getting louder. If the roof crashed in, it might smash through the floor and pin them in. It was getting hard to breathe. His eyes smarted. And the horse kept jerking its head back as he tried to cover its eyes.

"Here!" Patrick was at him again. "I've got this one fixed. Lead him out."

36

"Lead him yourself, I'm getting this one," Dan said.

Patrick swore blue and green and shouted, "Ye're as stubborn as the horses. Lead him and don't come back."

Dan obeyed. The blindfolded horse had to be pulled by main force. Dan got him to the doorway and surrendered him to one of the growing crowd. "Tie him up so he can't get back," Dan shouted and then turned back to the barn. Larry was leading another horse out, which meant there were only two to save. Patrick, he found, had sacked up the third. He growled when he heard Dan—for the smoke was getting too thick to see. "Take this one—and stay out, do you hear?" Patrick said roughly. "I'll bring the last."

"You come out now too, horse or no horse," Dan urged. He groped to the doorway with the animal and handed it over to a helper. Dan hesitated. Sparks were dropping down the hay chute. The smoke was so thick you had to stoop to breathe. But he had to turn back. Some impulse turned him. It was neither volition nor reason. He had to fetch Patrick. He could not endure to live if Patrick were burned alive.

In the dense smoke he bumped into something. "So it's you!" Patrick said and coughed. "Grab this halter and pull."

A wave of smoke enveloped them. Dan groped for the halter, blinded and choking. The horse was pulling him, or Patrick was pulling both. He couldn't tell. He hung on and suddenly he smelt air. He stumbled over the threshold, hearing voices, shouts. All was confusion. "Let go! Let go! I have him!" someone shouted.

Dan let go. Sallie was there. She had him by the arm and was taking him out into the sunlight. He felt choked and sick. "Where's Patrick?"

"He's right here," Sallie said. "Oh, you gave me a fright."

Shouts of "There she goes!" "Watch out, everybody!" were followed by a thudding sound and a quick crackle of flames. The rest of the roof had caved in.

37

Dan sat down on the grass. The nausea was departing. He saw Patrick lying down on the grass. Despite his sickness, Dan managed to ask about the house.

"You stay still," Sallie said severely. "There're lots of people looking after it. And here's the Fire Company."

"That's good," and Dan lay back on the grass in the shade of a maple. Sallie made sure that he was all right and then left him to see if she could help Mrs. Badger. Presently he heard a voice he knew, and looked up. There high above him stood Will Brewster.

Dan sat up in glad surprise.

"What do I see! Frenchy the hero!" Brewster's round face crinkled in a smile.

"Hero nothing. I'm not even singed. Who let you out?"

"Me myself."

"I thought you were tied to the chair in that office."

"I bit the rope in two," Brewster grinned. "No more office. No more city. Father's going to let me go to the bad in my own way."

Dan grinned at the unlikely idea. "Birds?"

Brewster nodded. "I came out to celebrate my freedom and maybe find something for my collection. I'm going to make a collection of every bird and nest and egg in the East, Dan. Do you have to stay by this bonfire till it's out?"

"No, let's take a sneak." Dan got to his feet feeling very little worse. "I've got something to show you."

Will was looking at the empty air. "See that? A Blackburnian warbler. My first this year."

"I think you make up these names just to impress me," Dan said smiling. Brewster's news was important. Mr. Brewster had wanted Will to go into his law office as earnestly as Judge French had wanted Dan in his. Somehow or other Will's decision was very comforting to Dan. It showed that

38

he was not the only one to be unreasonable, and the Judge admired Will Brewster as much as everyone did. Will was shy and accommodating, until it came to this principle, this devotion to his calling, and in that he was like iron. And now he had won the right to follow the leanings of his own nature.

Dan walked his friend home listening to Brewster's plans. He had already strung wire, barbed and tripled at the top, around the lower garden as a refuge for birds from cat and boy.

"The birds have discovered it already, Dan. They know it's safe. Father calls it my bird sanctuary."

"Your what?" Dan laughed at the impressive name as he opened the door to his room. "Enter! This is my sanctuary. I haven't let anyone in here for a week. I even make my own bed."

"So I see," said Brewster looking at the unmade bed. "What's that?" He nodded at a mound of something covered by a damp sheet.

"Guess."

"I don't have to guess. I can smell it."

Dan lifted back the sheet carefully and revealed a statuette of a deer, wounded, lying on its deathbed of forest floor, with every line proclaiming the pathos of this premature end.

Brewster stood and examined the clay figure in silent study. Dan said nothing. He had no need to hurry his friend's verdict. His fingers had brought out what his heart had felt on that hideous morning. His eyes had been able to carry the doe's subtleties of shape. During the week he had been discouraged to the point of giving up, but something had kept him from giving in, and he was glad. Whatever anyone else might think, this small statue was a consolation to him, a relief and satisfaction.

"You've got it," Brewster said at last. "It brings it all

39

back." He looked at his friend. "I guess you've decided to be a sculptor."

"That's about the size of it," Dan said. "But I'm not telling anybody."

"You don't need to—with that." Brewster walked around and studied the other side. "You're a deep one! Why didn't you tell me you were taking lessons?"

"I will when I start."

"You mean you did that without any lessons?"

"I don't even know who'd give them to me. I'm so green I didn't know the stuff dried out on you." Dan started lifting back the damp sheet. "But then nobody taught you to chase birds, either."

"That's right. I never thought of that. Just a born ornithologist—with a long way to go," Will Brewster laughed.

Dan stared at him. "At least we haven't anybody to blame for our lives but ourselves."

"That's what I like," Brewster said quietly.

"THE WOUNDED DEER," as Pamela dubbed the statuette, made a stirring impression upon the French family. It appealed particularly to Pamela under whose practicality lurked reserves of feeling. The forehint of talent shown in the turnip frog and confirmed by the dog's head was established in the doe. Here was anatomy and good composition and, most amazing of all, a sense of pathos. Where in the world had the boy got to know a deer in all its reality—wild, wounded, innocent?

Dan, goaded by this praise, told how he had come by his sad knowledge.

"I think you must take this to town and show it to somebody," Pamela said decisively.

Dan laughed. "Shall I walk up and down Tremont Street or is it best to stand on one corner?"

"You know perfectly well what I mean. Henry, who in Boston knows about statues?"

"The Cobb brothers, I fancy," said the Judge. "Even though they're architects, Cyrus Cobb employs architectural sculptors."

"Would you take it to him for an opinion?" Pamela asked.

"I can't today, and tomorrow I'm off to New York on that Easton case."

"Then I'll take it," Pamela said impulsively, her round face lengthening, as it did when she was decisive.

Dan listened. He was impressed, though he tried not to show it. It was very satisfying to have won his stepmother, the least likely conquest in the family circle. Her judgments, while often sharp, were always sincere. If she thought his statuette good enough to lug to town, he should feel encouraged. So on the following morning he drove Pamela to the station with the deer, carefully boxed, in her lap.

That day Dan spent putting a casement window in his room. This retreat where he worked as well as slept faced north and east and the winter temperatures were Spartan. Mornings when it was twenty below zero he would come down to breakfast and ask if he might not move for warmth into the ice-house. But in summer the room was correspondingly hot.

After the week of intense concentration on his deer going by nothing but intuition, it was a relief to use rule and plumb-line, pencil and saw. He had the right temperament for the job, the slow patient hand to carry out the behests of the quick sure eye. Nor did his wits wander often to Pamela's errand. The time he had agreed to meet her arrived swiftly. Even as she came down the train steps, he saw the verdict in her face, a victorious glint shining in her black eyes.

"Mr. Cobb was much interested, Dan," she told him. "He said he knew no one in Boston who could have done your deer, and only one man in New York—the Mr. Ward whose *Indian Hunter* is so much admired. He asked me whom you had studied under."

"Under Judge and Mrs. French, I hope you told him," Dan's voice was warm with relief at the trip's outcome. "He would hardly believe that you'd had no instruction. He recommended a Dr. Rimmer."

Dan was silent. Tuition cost money. Going into town cost money. This was getting serious. Had he actually meant to set all these consequences in motion when he carved the turnip? No, that was pure instinct. And the dog? That was competition got up by his father. But the deer? Yes, he was in earnest about the deer, and to stop being in earnest now was cowardice. He had not turned back from the plow when tempted. And this was very like it. Nor had he backed out of doing his duty in the burning barn. Why should he turn back now? And what would come of denying his one gift?

Pamela was telling him more of Mr. Cobb's advice, but Dan hardly listened. He had just made the decision. He would risk it because he had to. It was in him.

Next morning Dan was screwing on the hinges of his casement window. He was sitting astride the sill, engaged in holding the opened sash with his knee while making the hinge fast to the upright, when he saw a vision approaching on horseback.

He stopped to take in the picture—May Alcott, Bronson Alcott's fourth and likeliest daughter, tricked out in her Paris riding-habit, which she had no doubt worn in their park. The long skirt and close-fitting bodice were green and looked like velvet from where Dan stared. A green feather curled coquettishly over the brim of her straw hat, which failed to conceal her golden hair, luxuriant and glistening in the sun. She sat her horse as if she had just conquered Europe. Clothes certainly made a difference, Dan thought dizzily. Who ever would have thought that a daughter of a

43

perpetually impoverished philosopher would come back from abroad looking like a queen!

To Dan's delight the woman waved to him and then, surprisingly, turned her horse into the yard. Its hooves made holes in the spring turf. Dan expected to hear Pamela commanding May to take her horse off the lawn in outraged tones. "I'll be down," he called and rushed to avert the calamity. "Won't you come in?" he asked. "Mother's about the place somewhere."

"It's you I came to see, Dan," said the queen. "Father saw the statue of your deer and thought it most convincing. It moved him and he begged me to look at it. I wonder if you'd show it to me."

Dan helped her out of the side-saddle. "How did Mr. Alcott see it?" he asked as he took her into the parlor where the statue stood on a small table.

"He sat beside your mother in the train. She is so proud of your achievement. When she mentioned her errand in Boston father begged for a look. Father is very wise, in many ways, you know, Dan. He feels that you have a genuine gift. He hopes you will encourage it, for your own and Concord's sake. Father is very concerned with Concord's intellectual achievements."

May had been studying the deer while she talked. Now she walked around it in silence. Dan was undergoing a new experience. May, who had studied in the ateliers of Paris and copied paintings in the galleries of London, was examining his work professionally. Her few comments were impersonal, not so flattering as he had hoped, but not discouraging either. Now she pointed out a crack he had not seen in the deer's neck. "What did you use for armature?" she asked.

"What's that?"

"The skeleton." May looked at him with a smile. "Didn't

44

you know that every statue had to be supported by a framework inside?"

Dan shook his head. He was dumb.

"Yes, just like us," May said. "I'm afraid that this lovely thing will crumble and fall to pieces. It's a shame."

Dan felt sick. "There's no way of saving it?"

"Hardly, after the clay's dry." May felt the statue.

"What had you thought of trying next?" May inquired after a silence.

"Would a head be too difficult?" Dan asked. "My brother Will's coming back from a business trip and I know he'd offer himself as a sacrifice."

"You always have to try something harder than you think you can do to get ahead," May said. "Will you let me show you how to support a bust? I've some extra clay, too. I'm free this morning, if you'd like to come."

Dan's dark brown eyes warmed at the offer. "I'll be there as soon as I can hitch up."

Half an hour later Dan tied up Stubtail to the post in front of the Alcott home on Lexington Road. The old frame house, painted brown, and since there was no money for carpenters—enlarged and altered by Mr. Alcott himself, stood in the shade of two immense elms, the picture of peace. No passerby would have guessed how much gaiety and sacrifice, how much intellectual fermenting and feminine contrivance, simmered and boiled behind those walls.

Dan had visited here less than at the Emersons' or Judge Hoar's or other leading houses of Concord. This was unconsciously because of Pamela, for Bronson Alcott was the butt of her sharpest wit. Pamela was a practical housekeeper, Mr. Alcott the ineffectual provider, and this was a severe count against the man, no matter how kind a father, how inspired a teacher, how wise a philosopher, the man might be.

45

Judge French tried to blunt Pamela's darts of laughter by pointing out that Mr. Emerson, the wisest man in America, admired Mr. Alcott. The Judge commented on this educator's success with his own family. May's art classes were well attended. Anna was unselfish and kind, a thoroughly fine woman. Beth had been equally promising when she died. Louisa, it was true, sometimes perplexed those who had merely met her. She seemed the victim of impulse and of moods. The fact remained that she was nothing less than a heroine. She had expended her health and vitality in nursing the Civil War wounded. Now she was writing books, penning one after another, in an effort to support her family.

"That's just what I mean!" Pamela had exclaimed. "She's writing herself into her grave just because Bronson's persnicketiness won't permit him to do anything practical. I've no use for such a man."

Dan was glad, now that he was about to accept a favor from May, that he had not joined in the general village condemnation. He walked up to the house, wondering which door to knock. Louisa saw him coming and called, "Oh, Dan, May's studio's in the barn, but would you come here a moment?"

Her face, dark and tired, appeared in the doorway. "Excuse my not asking you in," she laughed. "I'm in working garb. I've a parcel I want sent. Since you go so near the station would it be an imposition?" She smiled one of her abrupt smiles. "You'll be careful of it? It's three years' work."

"All that one book?" Dan hefted the package, wax-sealed and addressed in a vigorous handwriting.

"The whole family's in it, so it's naturally long-winded," Louisa Alcott laughed.

"You're putting your family in a story?" To Dan this seemed a risky experiment.

"What else do I know so well?" Then her dark eyes shone

46

with a sudden violence. "Concord can make of it what it likes."

Dan promised to be careful of the precious package and went on to the barn. He was thankful that May was not so tempestuous in her moods. Yet he felt attracted to the passion he felt in this woman, the mania of devotion to her own people. It was almost a rebuke to his light-hearted approach to his work. Yet he had lost himself in the deer. Nothing superficial about that.

May had already procured a wooden base for his proposed bust of Will. Now she let Dan help her fasten an iron pipe upright as a central core of the head. Over it she curved a lead pipe and wired on little wooden crosspieces, which she called "butterflies." The clay was to go on this structural foundation.

Dan dragged over a washtub full of clay, kept moist by being sprayed and covered with cloths never allowed to dry. May showed Dan how to pull out a handful of the clay and pat small bits of it around the butterflies first, then adding and adding until the mass approximated the size of the bust desired.

"Do you guess or measure?" Dan asked.

May showed him her calipers. "You get every possible dimension. From nose to back of head. From ear to ear. Top of skull to base. Width of jaw, and so on and on, scores of measurements."

Dan felt strangely reassured. These dividers related this unknown effort called art to his carpentry. At once he felt at home. He did not mind taking a thousand measurements. Poor Will!

"Have sculptors ever been slain by their sitters?" he asked with a grin.

"What an idea! I never heard of it." May smiled. "I should think it possible, the moment the subject first sees what the

47

artist has made of him. Getting a likeness is a special gift, like absolute pitch in music."

"How do you go about getting it?" Dan asked.

"If I could teach that, I'd never lack pupils," May Alcott said. "It can't be taught. It's a matter of seeing. You transmit what you see to the clay through your fingers. Your fingers have to know how to obey your eye. But what is it your eye obeys? Your mental perception and that is very closely tied in with your sensibility, your conscience, the thing that is talking to you all the time. That's why it is important not to misuse your conscience. You must keep it honest and innocent in order to see honestly and clearly to the very depths of a person, and then your thumb transfers your insight to the clay and you have a likeness. I'm indebted to father for this. He follows everything back into the spiritual, and he's right."

Dan felt that he had never been so indebted to one person as to this daughter of Bronson Alcott. She had torn a hole in the blank wall that had seemed to confront him. Here he was ready to start a bust of his brother, and she had provided him with the rules, the first steps, and the encouragement. If Pamela ever tried to make jokes about this family again, he would have something to say.

May held out to him three tapering sticks, rounded at the end, made of some hard fine-grained wood, and very smooth. "They save your fingers," she explained.

He took them, turned them over, felt them, and handed them back.

"They're for you. I've others."

"You've already given me a lot." He wanted to pay for them.

"Let them be my good-luck gift," she said. "And please let me know when you finish the bust, so that I can come look at it."

48

Dan thanked her, promising to let her see the finished work, and carried the beginnings of Will's bust out to the wagon. He went back for the rest of the clay that May had given him with the tools. He walked on air. This was the real start. Now he was a sculptor with clay under his fingernails and some sound instruction to go on. He climbed up on the wagon in a dream—and then climbed down again. He had forgotten to unhitch the horses.

He looked around rather sheepishly hoping that nobody had seen. A dark head leaned out of the window and called, "Have you got my book?"

The blood rushed to his face! In his joyous concentration on May's instructions, he had forgotten everything else. Louisa's precious manuscript was lying up there in the studio. He hurried past the empty window ashamed, feeling unforgivable.

Louisa Alcott confronted him as he came back with the package, her face pale. She held out her hands for it. "Please give it to me."

"I'm sorry. I apologize," Dan said contritely. "I'll take it direct to the station."

"I shouldn't've asked you. I've not entrusted a letter to Father for twenty years. Please let me have it."

"Don't make me feel worse than I do," Dan said.

The dark woman with the sick face still held out her hand. "I have to go to the station myself later."

"Then let me drive you, Miss Alcott. I'll wait."

"I may change my mind and take it to the publisher myself."

Dan knew better than to give in; if he did, they would both feel badly about it. "May I ask what you call it?" he ventured.

The angry lines of her face changed. *Little Women.*

"That's a taking title," Dan observed.

49

"Do you think so? The family feels that it is a very indifferent title. Now let me have my manuscript, please."

"I wish I could oblige you, but it was entrusted to me by a young lady whom I very much admire, and nothing could induce me to part with it."

Miss Alcott stared. She was not used to being stood up to by men, and this one was a mere stripling. Tipping his hat, Dan left with the bundle.

"I forgot to say—it goes C.O.D." called Miss Alcott.

"I'll see to that," Dan called. The least he could do was pay the charges. He climbed into the wagon, exuberantly happy. What a morning!

CHAPTER

7

"MY FIRST SITTER!" Dan exclaimed as he shoved a chair into the light.

Will settled himself in the chair. "We should have a corps of historians here to immortalize the occasion. How do you want me to sit?"

"How do you usually sit?" Dan smiled. "Relax and tell me about the Chicago girls. I'm going to make a lot of measurements first. You don't have to look so military."

The occasion had an element of newness that neither of them realized, for the two brothers had come at last into an equality. It had been a stern chase, for Will was seven years older than Dan. Now Dan had caught up and was telling Will what to do.

Ever since Baby Dan could toddle, Will had been the leader—out of doors at Grandma French's place in Chester, New Hampshire, in Cambridge, everywhere. Even when Dan had taken to drawing on an old shed wall in Amherst, it was Will who had started it.

The two young men had as many differences as resemblances. While Will was a natural student, Dan regarded

51

books as dry. Will was quick-witted, Dan liked to dream along. Will was energetic, nervous, typically American; Dan functioned in a quieter manner. Will's nature was out-going and exploratory, Dan's somewhat in-going and content to ride the slow currents of his inner being. Each was practical, each idealistic.

In this summer of 1868, Will was twenty-five, a Harvard graduate, an ex-member of the Provincetown Coast Guard, and a business man about to launch out on his own in Chicago. It was unlikely that Dan would find a handsomer subject for a portrait unless he looked in the mirror. Both young men had expressive brown eyes, but Will's hair was black while Dan's was brown. Will's features were strongly modeled, and his eyes had a frank open expression which comes from a well-captained heart and a fine rectitude of living.

Since Will was busy in Boston he could give only the late afternoons to sitting. They used these times to catch up on each other's activities. Will talked of his future business plans, Dan reviewed the theatricals he had got up in Concord; both compared the girl situation. Will found the female Chicagoans tame as "gazelles," Dan described his latest find in Concord as pretty as a "coach dog." The sittings were interrupted by rude and frequent laughter. The ladies in question would have found their admirers something worse than irreverent.

Meanwhile the bust progressed. Will, having sponsored Dan's drawing, felt a proprietary pride in his pupil. It was Will's encouragement that led Dan to consider an offer of May Alcott's. May held a class in drawing on Monday, Wednesday, and Friday mornings for girls. Twenty-five were enrolled, all she could attend to. She suggested that she would make an exception for him, if he wished to study drawing. He had to study it somewhere she told him. Drawing was the foundation of painting—which was news to Dan —and also of sculpture—a matter he had never considered.

Dan talked it over with Will. "I'll feel a little lonely, don't you think?" Dan asked. "Like my namesake in the den of lions."

"But these are lionesses," Will said. "Very different."

"I love to be admired by one girl," Dan said. "And two is exhilarating. But twenty-five! Won't it get monotonous?"

"I wouldn't bother about admiration until you come to it," Will said.

"All right then, if you want to take the dark side of it. How much work can I get done with twenty-five girls snickering behind my back?"

"You could have a screen," Will proposed. "The way they do about hospital beds."

Both of them agreed, however, that it was only reasonable to take advantage of a skilled teacher, whose rates were not high, and who lived only two miles away. Pamela concurred. The Judge withheld an opinion but secretly smiled behind his beard. Sallie, however, was outspoken. She said that Dan would never live it down.

"You really don't know what you're getting into!" she exclaimed. "You can't even sit beside one without making the others jealous."

"A risk so small I hadn't even thought of it," Dan said.

"That's not the worst of it," Sallie cried. "You've shifted your attentions from one to another of at least half a dozen. What are you going to do about that?"

"*Ad astra per aspera,*" quoted the Judge gravely.

"I've always been told there was safety in numbers," Dan said. "Now I've got the numbers and you complain."

One wholesome advantage of these family bouts was that they left the problem debated stripped of all surprise. So when Dan's first lesson day arrived, he found himself accept-

53

ing the twenty-five young ladies on twenty-five chairs before twenty-five drawing-boards as a common phenomenon.

Fortunately he did not have to chose between empty chairs. He took the only one there was, beside a girl named Mary Wheeler who was serious enough about the work to drive in all the way from Nine Acre Corner. Her concentration helped him, in contrast with many of the others for whom "art" was a fill-in before marriage, like playing the piano, crocheting, and reading Tennyson in social groups.

Behind him there was a continual whispering.

"My dear, I'll never get that chin."

"Who did May say the gentleman is?"

"Hermes."

"Well, I don't see anything so wonderful about him. If he were a real boy, I'd call him cute."

"Oh, dear, are we supposed to count those curls?"

"I say we ask May to give us a live model."

Many snickers. "I know who you want. Judd Colgan."

"Not while Jim Melvin's around. Judd's the farm-boy type."

Then a lowered voice. "Why not—?"

And Dan would know they were discussing him. Not without reason. Hermes had neither thick brown hair, laughing eyes, nor a smile that magnetized you to him. Nor could he invite you to go rowing.

This was all good fun and Dan gave the supper table at home many laughs, imitating Florence Gillson's catty, "Did you *see* Grace in that trailing black silk last night? What *did* you think of it?" But it was not the best atmosphere for single-minded work, and after all he was using hard-earned strawberry money for these lessons.

One Saturday morning Dan took his sketch-block to the river. May Alcott had invited the class to choose some detail of Concord that each liked best, sketch it, and bring it in on

Monday. Dan knew that the river would provide his subject. It was practically a member of the family. He swam in it, skated on it, took his girls rowing on it, and sometimes strolled or lay beside it when he had something on his mind.

It was, he felt sure, the most restful river in creation. It suited his temperament, calm to the outward eye but mysterious within, occasionally given to high times, but companionable always and above all beautiful. The eye was delighted in every direction at every season. When he floated on it, he had a feeling of harmony as if all his desires would be granted and each become part of his life's experience.

But how pick out a favorite detail? He walked on and on, past the family property line, lured ahead yet giving up a dozen spots for the better one not yet come upon. Passing a boathouse he ran into Lucy Barrett, who often sat near him in drawing-class.

"Painting?" He noticed the daubed smock which concealed a figure that Sallie cruelly called "roly poly" but which he thought merely comfortable.

"Oh, Dan! Please, tell me something. Do you think it's prettier with one stripe or two?" She pointed to a rowboat she was decorating.

Dan said, "One," partly from conviction, partly because he wanted her company on the river. "How would you like to go boating?" he asked.

Lucy hesitated. "I promised to bake a sponge-cake."

"Just down to North Bridge and back. Help me decide what to draw."

Lucy fixed the bargain. "One hour and not one minute over." She took off the smock, fluffed her lovely blonde hair, and moved to the stern with the charm of good-nature in her dimpled face. Dan had noticed that she was one of the serious workers in May Alcott's class and determined to become better acquainted.

55

"Maybe you can tell me why Concord girls know how to do so many things," Dan said when they were well launched.

"More than other girls?" Lucy asked.

"They row and ride and skate and swim. They read Greek and write poetry and go to lectures. They bake and get up picnics and can shingle a hen-house or nail up curtains. They stretch carpets and act charades and plays and play the piano. And they adorn themselves in good taste."

"What an observer you are!"

"Oh, yes, and they flatter!"

"Not unless they want to. Are you comparing us with girls in Boston or in some town Concord's size?"

"I knew a few in Amherst and Cambridge and Exeter and in Concord they're twice as able."

"Daniel French! That's an awful thing to say!"

"Excuse me, I take it back,—but why?" Dan asked disarmingly.

"No girl wants to be just able."

"I didn't say 'just' able. Concord girls do all these things and still are feminine."

"That's better," Lucy smiled. "Now what do you mean by feminine?"

"What you are now!" Dan looked at Lucy and laughed.

"Now you're spoiling it, you're making it personal!"

Dan smiled. "When was that an affront to a girl?"

"Oh, dear, you know too much!" Lucy exclaimed.

It was an exquisite tickling pleasure to spar like this in the open sunshine on the placid river. Dan forgot that he had started out to draw. He delighted in Lucy Barrett's moods, real and assumed. She was far from being merely fluffy, in spite of their soap-bubble chatter and her giggles. Her family had had its roots in Concord almost as long as any, and she had solid training in matters of education and

56

character. Leaning back with her elbows on the stern, washed in the June sun, she was prettier than any crayon the class was likely to draw and the picture she made was framed by the greens and blues of the forenoon sky.

They came in sight of the run-down North Bridge where the farmers of the neighborhood, pledged to assemble on a minute's notice, had halted the British forage parties.

"That ramshackle bridge is going to drop someone into the water someday," Dan observed.

"There's talk of building a new one for the anniversary."

"What anniversary?"

"April 19, 1875."

"That's nearly seven years off," Dan said. "Pity they couldn't've postponed the fight twenty-four hours. Then we could all have celebrated together. April 20th is my birthday."

"Oh, the conceit of man!" Lucy cried. "Wanting history rearranged just to celebrate his birthday!"

"Merely a passing suggestion," Dan chuckled. Life was good. With a charming girl saying things she scarcely meant in the downpour of gentle sunlight on a Saturday morning on the river, life was very good indeed. "Why did they put up that monument on the British end of the bridge?"

Lucy laughed. "That's what Ebby Hubbard wanted to know. It made him *so* mad! He said he'd give a thousand dollars to have a statue put up in the right spot. I do think they should put a cannon or something at our end to show what happened."

"They fired flintlocks, not cannon."

"I know, but you can't have just a pile of old muskets to mark the place. It would look so messy."

"Why not one of the farmers?"

"I don't think that would look very romantic. The minute men didn't even have uniforms, and besides they weren't on horseback. Whoever heard of a statue of a soldier not on horseback! It's the horse I always like to look at best."

Dan was silent. Girls were funny about things of this kind. Why weren't the farmers hurrying from their plows, as romantic as the redcoats looking like lobsters in their uniforms? But you couldn't make them admit that. They didn't understand that it wasn't what you saw but the way you saw it that made a thing romantic—or commonplace, for that matter. Those farmhands were summoned to death and ruin on that April morning. That was stirring enough. You didn't need gold lace and a horse. They didn't add a thing to your feelings, and it was your feelings that made a thing romantic, or tragic.

Lucy felt for her watch pinned on her left breast. "Daniel French, we've been out an hour already!" she cried. "I just knew this would happen."

"I hoped it would," Dan laughed outright.

"I'll never trust you again."

"Serious?" he asked with mock alarm.

"You'll see!" But she had to lean over the side of the boat to hide her smile and Dan saw it in the water. He smiled back at it, glad that girls were girls.

Next morning Dan let his father and Pamela and Will and Sallie go to church without him, despite protestations. Some obscure instinct was prompting him to make the plaster cast of Will's finished bust alone. May Alcott had described the operation and he had written the procedure down. If it turned out well, all right; if it didn't, the fewer observers the better. As in any other phase of personal living, he wanted to master it himself.

Before the Meeting-house bell stopped tolling, Dan had assembled the bag of plaster of Paris that May Alcott had given him, the pieces of iron pipe needed to strengthen the

58

outside of the mold, and the pieces of brass, which May called shims, and which were to make the separation of the mold possible. Also he found some green soap to brush on the inside of the mold. He almost forgot the most important thing of all—an old sheet to lay on the floor. Pamela had an obsession about dirt. His bedroom was not safe from inspection, either.

He forgot time, place, setting, everything—in the concentration on the plaster. Its consistency had to be stiffer than corn pudding, but not quite so stiff as cheese. Finally, after running back and forth for water through his parents' bedroom to Pamela's dressing-room, he got the plaster just right to apply. But in the excitement and breathlessness of it all, he forgot to take away the brass shims until the plaster had set.

This was his first set-back, and made him feel forlorn after an hour's tense labor, for now it would be difficult to get them out at all. To make matters really uncomfortable, he heard movement downstairs, then on the stairs, and abruptly Pamela's voice, a shade upset, cried, "Dan! What *have* you been doing?"

"Casting Will's head."

"But look at my matting!"

He stepped out into the hall and into her room.

"You might suppose a hodcarrier had been plastering the ceiling."

Dan now saw the broad white trail made by his impassioned steps to the water faucet.

"I'm sorry, I'll clean it up."

"Really, Dan!" came indignantly from the dressing-room where the wash-basin was a mess of green soap and blueing. "I've never seen such a mess! It is most careless and thoughtless—"

"Mother!" Judge French could be very authoritative.

"Dan says he's sorry. It's just a little dirt. I'll help him clean it up. Dan how's it coming?"

"I'm just finishing the mold," Dan said uncomfortably, for he was irritated by the forgotten shims and the plaster-tracking. His mother was right. He had been abominably careless. "I'll do the cast this afternoon."

"And please get your water from the pump!" Pamela requested.

She closed the door to take off her Sunday garments. Between undressing and dressing, she found time to clean up the plaster and the wash-basin. This made Dan feel worse than ever, for he had wished to make amends himself.

Before supper time he had taken the cast. It was disappointing. He sat down before it and for a while was sunk in gloom. This thing of being a sculptor was much more than he had suspected. He had a long row to hoe. As Mr. Cobb told Pamela, he needed instruction.

The bust proved it. And before he paid tuition he must have money. Then he could go to Boston or New York for lessons. What were those instructors' names? Dr. Rimmer. . . . Mr. Ward.

When Pamela came quietly into the room to beg forgiveness for her outburst—and bring him some ice-cold lemonade —she found Dan sober but not discouraged. The Judge looked in, and under his cheerful words was concern lest his youngest lose hope and spirit.

But Dan, as had always been his way in crises, said little. If sensitive, he was resilient. That evening, instead of hunting up Lucy Barrett, he started making charcoal sketches of the farmer they spoke of at the Bridge.

CHAPTER

8

A YOUNG MAN'S development should, no doubt, be as orderly and persistent as the sun's progress across the sky. But it isn't. Rather it is more like the growth of a tree. It has its winters and its springs.

And so with Dan. After the success of the Wounded Deer and the drawing lessons and the failure of Will's bust, Dan engaged in no more ambitious work for a while. He needed to catch up with himself. He worked hard on the farm. His social life became a career. He enjoyed himself.

Yet the next season was budding where the old one had fallen off. In those little sketches he had made of the North Bridge, there was a certain vitality, a certain picturesqueness, and he lived with them in his mind.

Judge French said nothing. Patrick said nothing. They were two wise men. But when Dan asked if he might put a skylight into the little room back of the shop and use it as a studio, the Judge was overjoyed. Then one day Dan slipped off to Boston without telling his errand. The new season had begun.

Dr. William Rimmer. The name had stayed in the back of Dan's mind since that day, a year ago, when his mother had borne the Wounded Deer to Mr. Cobb in Boston. But Dr. Rimmer was an elusive person to run to earth, living as he did three lives—as doctor, as lecturer at the Massachusetts Institute of Technology, and as sculptor. While Dan hunted him down the comedy of the situation didn't escape him. When an invalid wanted the doctor, the good doctor would be haranguing his classes across the river. When a student needed to see him, he might be either in his studio, his office, or the room where he gave drawing lessons, or— home in bed.

Dan cornered him in his home. At once he felt confidence in this alert-eyed man who talked art with his sleeves rolled up. Dan explained that he had dropped out of May Alcott's class since it was composed almost wholly of young ladies awaiting marriage. He wanted to sweat at his art work.

Dr. Rimmer smiled. "In my class the proportion is not much better—three men, twenty-five ladies."

"What's up?" asked Dan. "The women going art-mad?"

"Do you realize that the women of your generation are the first to find time on their hands? First it was pioneering, then the excitements of making a nation, and then the War. Now they have leisure, and it's a new toy. They tinkle the piano, design draperies, and paint sunsets. We men have had the arts to ourselves for a long time. Now we'll have to exert ourselves or be beaten. Women always prove better than men at anything they put their minds to." The doctor came down to cases. "Why do you wish to study with me?"

"Because I can't keep away from clay," Dan said. "When I see a dog I think, 'I must get that pose.' When I'm working on our farm, I know my interest isn't all there."

"You are," the doctor scrutinized Dan, "about twenty?"

"Yes, sir, I was nineteen last April."

"High time you were making the plunge. What practice have you had?"

Dan told him about the turnip, the dog's head, the Wounded Deer, the bust. He did not mention the sketches of the soldier-farmer.

"Tell me about your life before you carved your turnip," the doctor said with a thoroughness that delighted his listener.

Dan told of his delight in being outdoors, in identifying birds, in stuffing them. He mentioned his carpentry.

"And play? What have you played at?"

Dan smiled and confessed about all the charades, tableaux, the beautiful constructions of the theater.

Dr. Rimmer nodded. "Excellent!" he exclaimed unexpectedly. "The birds have taught you to use your eyes, the carpenter shop to use your hands, and the stage to show you that art is the heightening of life. Good. With observation, manual skill, and a love of form, we have something to work on if we have, shall I say, perseverance?" The doctor's glance was quizzical.

"Father's taught me to finish what I begin," Dan said.

So he was admitted to Dr. Rimmer's class.

The doctor-sculptor set his students to studying the human body—first with colored charts, life size, to reveal the interlocking marvel of bones and muscles and organs. He had imported a plaster cast showing a man without his skin. He also had a skeleton. He hung his charts in a line, posed the skeleton next, placed the plaster cast next, and then stood his young man, as nature made him, at the end of the line.

When the model flexed his arm, the doctor used his other exhibits to show what was happening beneath the skin. "Nature did a marvelous job of packing," he said, pointing out the thrifty way in which the muscles took advantage of their

63

space. He was much in earnest about tendons, ligaments, muscle-pull. He had his students draw every position, in motion and in repose.

"Ladies and gentlemen," Dr. Rimmer said in his exact but interested voice, "as usual, the visible depends upon the invisible. A sculptor must understand the framework of his model. Beauty is only skin-deep, some fool said. That is untrue. Beauty is as deep as the mind can go. My effort will be to show you how to build the beauty your sight brings you, and remember what I tell you—insight is sight into."

Dan had never heard such stimulating talk. He made a blackboard for use at home. He entertained the family with reports of goings-on in the classes.

"It sounds terrible to me!" Sallie exclaimed after one particularly detailed and vivid description.

"What's so terrible about it?"

"Oh, I don't know exactly. Drawing nudes, I guess. Why do artists always have to draw nudes?"

"Would you rather we stick to suits and dresses?" Dan inquired.

"Well, people don't appear without their clothes on," Sallie said.

"You can be sensible about nudity if you want to," Dan said. "Nobody in art class gives a hoot. The ladies, thank heaven, don't giggle or blush. We have to see how the machine's made. And we can draw a man or a woman as God designed the creature, as impersonally as if we were drawing a tree."

"Just the same," Sallie said, "artists are known not to have any morals."

The Judge thought it time to step in. "That's simply not so," he said sternly. "Dr. Rimmer is one of the most moral men. I inquired as to his character, naturally. I'm surprised,

64

Sallie, to hear you judge a person by hearsay before you have the facts."

Sallie swallowed the rebuke. But her true feelings went far deeper. She could not cry out to Dan, "You've always been my baby brother! Now you've gone out into the world, away from me," for in her saner moods she was thankful Dan had done just that and was growing up.

Dan patted his sister's shoulder. "Don't worry, Sis."

"I'm not worrying about *you!*" Sallie said.

Dan and his father exchanged glances of understanding. Judge French took great comfort in his son.

New Year's passed and St. Valentine's Day approached. As a child Dan had loved to get valentines. For a while he supposed that the post office had been started in order to hand out these anonymous paper-laced missives. His first mystery was guessing who loved him so outspokenly.

This February he sighed at the number he would have to get and send. His interest centered in one girl. Ever since that Saturday morning on the river, he had been seeing more of Lucy Barrett and seeing more in her, too. She was a fine-looking girl and a good companion. Things had gone to such lengths he stopped entering those tell-tale words, "Walked home with Lucy" in his diary. Once he had absent-mindedly left this diary downstairs and his father had written in an absurd entry. Dan was willing to bet his father had not read a word in the book, but it was quite wrong to tempt Pamela or Sallie!

For weeks, Dan worked on the valentine for Lucy as secretly as he had made the Wounded Deer. Nothing like it had ever been seen, he was sure. He hoped Miss Barrett had a sense of humor, or she might take it as an indirect proposal. In about twenty years, he thought gloomily, if his

65

progress were not interrupted he might be able to count on an income warranting a proposal.

The subject of this valentine, Dan decided, must have come from his bird-watching days with Will Brewster. For he had caught a wooing owl in the very act of tender attention to his hoped-for mate. His wing was spread over the lady owl's shoulder, his claw rested gently on her claw, his head was bent to communicate his intentions, while she listened to him with every evidence of acquiescence.

Dan had chuckled a hundred times as he modeled the feathers to a Sunday-best perfection and brought the last touch of brimming sentiment to the lady owl's eyes. But he sobered when he had cast these owls sitting so snugly side by side. He had carved "St. Valentine's Day" on the base, intending a light but charming joke. But this was not quite a joke. Thanks to his ornithology and Dr. Rimmer's emphasis on anatomy, the clasped claws and the amatory leer, while amusing, were so sure of structure and eloquent that Dan was afraid Lucy would read too much in so elaborate a valentine. Or, if Lucy did not, what of others who were certain to see it? Also, this was his best work to date, and he could not reconcile himself to letting it come to rest on Lucy's mantelpiece. No, he must use this to get ahead. It was almost two years since he had done the Wounded Deer. Aside from the five dollars that his cousin Annie Keyes had paid him for a medallion, his money was coming chiefly from his strawberries. He ought to be able to sell these owls for ten dollars. Not much, but a beginning. Lucy should never know what she had missed; he would buy the most lavish valentine in Boston for her on the morrow.

Next day, with the same secrecy which always characterized his major moves, Dan carried the cast to Boston with him. But he did not show it to Dr. Rimmer. The good doctor did not lean towards sentiment. Instead he took it to

66

Williams and Everett, Fine Art Dealers on Washington Street.

"Mr. Williams is engaged," the clerk said. "Will you state your business and I'll carry him the message."

Dan opened the valise and brought out the owls, sitting six inches high and looking, in the cold glare of a business transaction, rather silly. "I'd like to sell this cast," he said, wondering now if this important firm would offer him five dollars.

The clerk glanced at it and said, "It's too late for Valentine's Day."

"Yes, I know," Dan said. "But there'll be another next year." If it was refused Pamela would be glad to have it, he thought. She had exclaimed over it and his father had been definitely impressed, saying that it showed how much he had got from his study with Rimmer.

"I think you'd better leave it," the clerk said. "I wouldn't care to interrupt Mr. Williams about it now."

At this moment Mr. Williams appeared from the inner recesses. He was a spare man with glasses fastened to his buttonhole by a black ribbon. "What is it the young man wants?" he asked the clerk.

"He has a curio to sell, sir."

"I made it," Dan said modestly.

Mr. Williams took up the cast and examined it while Dan tried to read in that expanse of face some evidence of his impression. But the dealer's face was as immobile as the owls. "You made it," he said at last. "Then why no name?"

Dan flushed. He had not thought of that. "I put the title on instead. Nobody puts names on valentines."

Mr. Williams set it down as you might set down a tumbler from which you had finished drinking. "A nice little thing," he said, "but I don't know what we should do with it. We deal in names, you know, Mr. French. Most of our customers

67

know nothing about art, but they do overhear names. Make
a name for yourself, and then come back and I shall be glad
to consider your work."

His monologue was interrupted by the slamming of the
door. A younger man took off his greatcoat briskly, looking
at Dan. He was the younger partner.

"Oh, Everett," resumed Mr. Williams. "This is Mr.
French of Concord. He's been trying his hand and brings
us this little piece. I tell him to make a name for himself
and then sign his work. He hasn't signed this."

Mr. Everett took up the owls. "So I see. Rather a pity, too.
Why did you render the feathers so over-emphatically?" he
asked Dan. He set the figures down and walked away, still
looking at them.

"I tell Mr. French that we sell reputations," Mr. Williams
re-entered the conversation.

"Of course," Mr. Everett concurred. "Artists bring us their
wares, charming things, but they would only sit on our
shelves if we did not insist on reputation. *That's* the com-
modity."

"How do you get a reputation?" Dan asked. "It has to
begin somewhere."

"True, very true," Mr. Williams said profoundly.

"It's the artist's look-out, not the dealer's," Mr. Everett
explained. He picked up the owls and carried them to the
bay window. "In sculpture the reputation starts usually after
the sculptor is dead. Don't you agree, Williams?"

"In nearly every case."

"Mr. Ward's still alive," Dan said, "and he's famous."

Mr. Williams had joined Mr. Everett in the window. Dan
saw only their backs. The clerk, uninterested, was writing
in a ledger. Dan heard one of the men say "Plimpton?" His
hopes rose. They were evidently considering his statuette.

Presently Mr. Everett and Mr. Williams walked back. "I

agree with my partner," Mr. Everett said. "There is very little we can do with your piece. Yet it has a certain pleasing quality. We are ready to take a risk if you, in turn, will sell us the rights to it for $50."

Dan was surprised, also he was vague about rights. "Which rights do you wish?" he asked.

"That's simply a phrase in the contract," Mr. Everett said. He had begun cleaning his nails as if the subject had lost interest.

"It means the right to reproduce," Mr. Williams said patiently. "You've brought us a plaster of Paris cast. Naturally we cannot do anything with that. There are other media, you know."

"I'm afraid I'll have to cut this short," Mr. Everett said to his partner. "I'm due at the Norths in twenty minutes."

"One moment," Mr. Williams said. "If Mr. French accepts our offer, you can put your signature on the contract before you go." Both dealers looked at Dan.

It was an agonizing moment. Something stood in the way. Dan felt hesitant about saying *yes* if these people were going to make copies of his work. "Instead of selling it outright, could I let you make copies and be paid so much on each copy you sold?" he asked.

"A royalty?" Mr. Everett said. "A very wide-awake proposition, I'm sure. You should institute it among sculptors, Mr. French. It will revolutionize the trade, I'm sure." He picked up the owls to hand back to Dan. "But we cannot go into any such matters. That's quite aside from our practice. Thank you very much for allowing us to see—"

"Then I'll have to accept the offer you made," Dan said.

"There's no 'have-to' about it," Mr. Everett said. "I've just induced my partner to assent to the risk. I'm certainly not going to persuade you."

"I'm persuaded," Dan tried to smile.

69

"In that case, Clark," Mr. Everett said to the clerk, "Form B, in triplicate, at once."

"I congratulate you, Mr. French," Mr. Williams said.

Dan congratulated himself. He rode home on a pink cloud. He had made $50 for a small outlay of money for materials; as for time and ideas, he had oceans of each.

The family was at supper. He was half bursting with his news, but it was unlike Dan to burst, and he had eaten to dessert before he found the easy opening to say, "I sold my owls today. To Williams and Everett for $50."

Sallie recovered first. "Oh, Dan! How wonderful! And *fifty* dollars! Think of it."

"Are you sure that was enough?" Pamela asked.

"Oh, *Mother!*" Sallie said.

"It's the boy's first sale!" Judge French remarked at once. "Congratulations, Dan. Which one of them did you see?"

Dan gave an account of the sale, and Sallie repeated her delight at his wringing such a sum from those "skinflints".

But two days later the Judge came home looking tired. After supper, when Pamela had him alone, she said, "Did something go wrong in the office, Henry?"

"No, my dear."

"Then what is the matter?"

The Judge looked around then lowered his voice. "Will you promise to say nothing to anyone, if I tell you?" Long ago he had found that Pamela was as safe as a strongbox if he extracted her promise.

"If I have to," Pamela said.

"Well, yesterday I went to Williams and Everett to buy back Dan's owls, if possible. I knew what was in their minds when they mentioned Plimpton. They said they had sold them and would not tell me where. So I went to Plimpton, whom I know, and he said he'd paid a thousand dollars for them."

"A thousand!" Pamela's eyes glinted dangerously. "That's worse than I dreamed!"

"That's only the beginning," the Judge said. "Plimpton's starting with a thousand copies which he expects to retail at three dollars apiece. He thinks they'll have a great vogue. He told me that it's the most original and taking piece he's recently handled."

"Poor Dan! They'll stare at him from every shop window in town!" Pamela cried. "At least he will get some reputation out of it."

"No, his name isn't on the cast."

"How well do you know Plimpton?" Pamela demanded. "Well enough to persuade him to pay Dan a little royalty? Even ten cents a copy would be so encouraging."

The Judge shook his head. "Business is business, my dear. We can't ask alms."

Pamela's black eyes flashed. "Why are men such pigs! Alms! If it weren't for Dan he wouldn't be able to sell the owls at all! It's only fairness to pay him something."

"A contract is a contract, sweetheart. Dan signed and that's the end of it. If businessmen were to reconsider every paper they signed for sentiment's sake, where would they be?"

"I'm talking about justice, not sentiment," Pamela said. "It's pure theft to take advantage of a boy who doesn't know the value of his work." She rose and vindictively pinched off a dying leaf from a geranium. "Pirates and highwaymen! That's all they are. Poor Dan, it breaks my heart!"

9

HAVING WATCHED his son through the years that tell best what is to follow, the Judge felt confident that Dan would be at first chagrined, then angry, then stimulated to further work by the news from Plimpton and Company. And in just that order, Dan suffered these emotions.

"You know," he said to his father, "until somebody buys what you create, you feel as if you were standing on only one leg. Now I have two."

In his angry disappointment, he thought of revenge, of doing another pair of owls, *signed,* so good that they would put Plimpton's on the shelf. But Dan could not remain in a vengeful mood for ten minutes. A comic idea came to him. He'd do a pair of hyenas laughing at his pair of owls. But it was simply an idea and passed. And suddenly the stimulus began to work. He would drown his regret in excellence. He would do something ten times as good as the owls.

Characteristically, he kept this vow to himself; but his family felt the difference in him. Dan the delightful, Dan the laugh-maker, the gay, the good, the mischievous and affectionate, popular and undecided, became Dan the sculptor.

Asking Dr. Rimmer he found that busts paid the biggest money—busts of people so eager to go down in posterity they were not only willing to pay, they would sit for hours and hours.

"What do you mean by big money?" Dan had asked.

"That depends," Dr. Rimmer answered. "Fifty dollars, a hundred, a thousand. It makes a difference who's doing it, how much the victim can pay, and how honest the sculptor. The flattered subject is naturally more delighted to pay than the head you have treated seriously, and is the best advertisement for you. That patron is always hauling people in off the street to see this marvelous work of Mr. Daniel French."

Dan's enthusiasm waned a little. "What is flattery?" he asked. "Removing the wart from the subject's nose?"

"No, art deals with a different sort of realism from that. I'd say that flattery is removing the cupidity from the subject's mouth. Sitters with so honest a feature as a wart do not feel sorry for themselves. It's the defacements of the soul, which they themselves should have removed, that they wish omitted."

"Is it flattery to try to see the best in the subject?" Dan pursued.

"That sounds permissible," Dr. Rimmer conceded, "if you stop short of a halo. Flattery is gratifying your sitter's vanity. It's trying to ingratiate yourself with him by lying. You can't be an honest artist and a liar at the same time, that's self-evident. Knowing you, I don't believe you're going to have any trouble with this temptation."

"You mean honest but poor?"

"I mean earnest and successful. You're the kind who keeps learning, the only kind there's any hope for, and you know better than to expect to be famous overnight."

"No, I give it a year," Dan's eyes smiled.

"That's right, always expect it the next year," Dr. Rimmer, who was rarely familiar, patted Dan on the shoulder, then ushered him out. "Begin with bas reliefs," he called.

So Dan did, and Sallie offered to sit for him.

"Which of your nine expressions do you want me to do?" Dan asked.

"Nine?" Sallie laughed. "I thought I had only three."

"No, there's Sallie the hat-trimmer, with a row of pins in her mouth, or Sallie the wooed-one gazing at Edward the Perfect—"

"You needn't go on!" Sallie interrupted. "I don't want to be anything but myself and considerably prettier."

Dan shook his head. "No prettier. I'm honest Dan and I does 'em as I sees 'em. Besides, you're beautiful now so why bother about being prettier?"

"Taffy!" Sallie exclaimed, pleased. "I thought Dr. Rimmer told you you musn't flatter your subjects."

"Wait till you see," Dan said ominously.

When the relief was finished the family agreed that it was a beautiful likeness, and Sallie could not take her eyes from it. She, who had never done anything distinguished, was distinguished now. Yes, and beautiful, and it wasn't flattery. Those lines and curves that Dan had seen were there. He had seen deeper than her own gazings in the glass, that was all.

The family pride in this achievement had a most unexpected result. Aunt Ann Brown said that she must have a bust of her husband, the same Uncle Simon who had thought Dan had lost his mind when he declined the law. Did Dan think he could make a bust?

Concealing any trepidation from his aunt, Dan said yes.

And what would a suitable remuneration be? After the experience with Williams and Everett, Dan determined never again to price his services too low. He figured that

$100 would be suitable. When this figure also suited his aunt, Dan tried to appear imperturbable. But he was far from composed as he made his armature and carried the clay to his uncle's home. This had to be good. Not only an immense sum, the biggest yet, was at stake, but a real opportunity. If pleased, Simon Brown would never stop talking about it.

The elderly gentleman found sitting an invitation to talk. His favorite subject was Dan's mother, Anne Richardson. "There never was another woman like your mother, Dan. It's from her you got your brown eyes and that head of hair. I don't suppose you remember the day you sat between her and me at church. You were only four or five. You were pretty wriggly and when she tried to keep you still, you said, 'But, Mama, how'm I going to see the people if I don't turn round?' "

After a few sittings, Dan wished he could do the bust laughing. For when he laughed, his uncle softened up into the most kindly of old men.

"I remember another time. You were playing on the floor with your blocks and suddenly looked up and said, 'Mama, what would you do was your chillun all dead? Wouldn't you be a pity—mercy sakes!' "

"Morbid little thing!" Dan laughed.

"No," said his uncle seriously. "All children talk about such things. They pick them up from us, I suppose. You never know what a child's taking in. Or what he'll do next. Like your putting Chester in your name. Now whatever possessed you to do that?"

"I don't suppose there was any one reason," Dan said thoughtfully. "I found out that most boys had three names and felt kind of left out. Then I got tired of having my initials stand for *darned fool*. It's funny father didn't think of that. He usually thinks of everything. And then our

75

grandma's place at Chester was heaven. I guess it just simply was the best name to take when I decided to have another name."

"Well, I never heard of a boy taking it on himself to name himself over again," the old man laughed so that he changed his pose. But the bust was coming along. Dan's telegraphy from eye to hand was getting surer, and he was grateful that his uncle did not interfere by offering suggestions. In fact, he prided himself on saying, "I always give a knowin' horse free rein."

One day near the end he called his wife in to see. "You never knew you married a man like that, did you, Ann?"

"It's precisely the man I've been living with," Aunt Ann said pertly. "Dan, you've done wonders. I'm proud of you."

Dan too was elated. He had surpassed himself. He remembered Dr. Rimmer's saying "Blessed is the artist who has no idea how he does it," and felt that way. The figure had grown almost unaccountably. It made Dan feel humble.

After the portrait of Uncle Simon, a fierce desire to grow possessed Dan. He seized on subjects new to him. When his brother Will wrote of the Chicago fire, Dan did a small figure of Mrs. O'Leary's cow in the act of kicking over the fateful lantern. It was in his nature to chuckle over Dickens, since his own humor was as quick and sensitive as a hound's nose: he picked Sairy Gamp as his first Dickens figure, then went to Cambridge to make a bust of Will Brewster's father —at a new high of $175.

His twenty-first birthday, April 20, 1871, fell into the midst of this new activity, both as an incitement and a reminder. The family gave him a "freedom party" to which all the pretty girls in Concord were invited.

Dan had to make a speech. "This is a melancholy occasion—" The handsome and totally unspoiled social lion of the evening waited until they had finished laughing. "These

76

sounds betoken no pity for my aging self—" More laughter. "These piles of gifts imply that you think it worth almost any sacrifice to get me off your hands." More roars. "I have one request to make. During my few remaining years, I would like the girls to wear flowers in their hair and be just as beautiful as tonight." Appreciative applause. "In conclusion, I hope soon to open a studio in the Town Hall. I hereby invite all of you girls to visit me in that studio, *singly*." Since Dan was the most trusted and truthworthy youth imaginable, that "singly" brought the loudest laughs of the evening and Dan sat down.

Miss Ellen Emerson represented her family at the party. As she was leaving she said to Judge French, "Father was sorry he could not come. He wished me to congratulate you on having so fine and promising a son."

"Please thank Mr. Emerson and tell him that it is the atmosphere he has created here in Concord that exerts such a good influence on us. We are all more promising than we ever should have been without him."

"You may be sure I'll tell father that."

The Judge smiled. "It will hardly come to him as a surprise."

"By the way," Miss Emerson said, "you might advise Dan to exhibit his owls and some other work at the Cattle Show. Ann Brown and I are the Committee on Art."

"This sounds like collusion," Judge Henry said, knowing he was speaking to the most honest woman in Concord.

"Oh, we'll lean over backwards *not* to give him the prize," Ellen Emerson said, smiling. "But not to the point of cracking our spines."

Finally the last guest left, and Dan, flushed and excited by so much joy, flung himself down by the table piled with gifts. "There are two sides to this," he said soberly. "What'll I do to repay you and everybody for it all!"

"Well," said the Judge in his most judicial solemnity, "after I send the women to bed, you might come help me with the dishes."

"Dearest," Pamela patted his cheek, "the dishes were done hours ago. Did you think I was going to have you spend the rest of the night doing housework? All you have to do is pay for the maids I had in."

"There, Dan, you have marriage in a nutshell," the Judge said. "Love and finances. I just mention it because legally now you are a man."

"You must also have someone to marry," Sallie said.

"I don't think tonight has made the choosing any easier," Dan remarked.

"I trust you preferred my gift to all the others," said the Judge.

"Oh, Father, if you're going to be silly, I'm going to bed," Sallie laughed.

Dan looked at his father's present—three large photographs of masterpieces by the sculptor Thorwaldsen. They were inspiring. Pamela had bought him Winckelmann's *Ancient Art*. His grandmother had sent Lady Hamilton's *Attitudes*, a book of drawing for young artists. "It looks as though you folks were going to drive me to—well something or other," he murmured smiling. "It's wonderful to have such a family." The shine in his eyes was more likely happiness than tears. But when Pamela kissed him goodnight, she hugged him close and whispered in his ear, "We are so proud, so proud, my dear."

And when Dan went to his room he found a letter on the pillow in his father's hand. He read it slowly:

"My dear Dan,

All the success which a good God can give, in business or the acquisition of worldly goods, can bring no

78

such comfort and satisfaction to a man as to see his children good and prosperous. . . .

To you, I think, many talents have been committed. . . .

I deem an artist's life higher and better than that of the professional or business man, if lived in the true spirit of grace which the love of art should inspire. . . .

He is happy who can combine his labors for his daily bread with constant progress in an art which makes visible and embodies conceptions of beauty and perpetuates in marble the evanescent faces of our friends. . . .

So with the hope that a good childhood may go on into a noble and prosperous manhood, you have the blessing of your

Father"

Dan sat on the bed with the letter in his hand, tired, happy, thankful, and full of promises he could not speak.

THE CATTLE SHOW grounds along the river were noisy with moos and bleatings and bellowings of the animals, with people's talk, and the Concord Band. Whether he had a heifer to show or not, everybody attended for everyone was interested in jelly or pickles if not in sows and hogs. All the stored-up exuberance of summer combined with the release from the toil of harvest made for jollity. Dan and Patrick and Judge Henry and Mr. Alcott and Mr. Emerson —with their diverse ages and diverse temperaments—all came to enjoy with their women folk the neighborly goings-on.

On a table in the main shed under a sign lettered ART EXHIBIT stood a water color of Henry Thoreau's birthplace by Mary Wheeler; a copy, in oils, of a Turner by May Alcott; some drawings by members of May's class; and two casts by Daniel Chester French—the owls, and a dog.

Dan kept away from this vicinity. In fact he was busy making mischief. His friend Cy Hubbard was going West for a month to buy horses, and Dan had persuaded him that he ought to discover which of his girl friends cared for him most.

"Here comes Annie Damon," Dan poked his partner. "You haven't broken the sad news to her yet."

"Oh, Dan! I've got a trade-last for you!" cried Annie, a buxom girl in a fresh print dress as pink as her complexion.

"I've got one for you—last go," said nimble-witted Dan. "Someone after my scalp?"

"No, why should they be? This is a beautiful compliment. I was looking at your lovely owls and I overheard Alice Prescott talking to a girl from Lincoln about you. Alice pointed you out, and the Lincoln girl said 'If he'd make a statue of himself it would be the most beautiful of all.' How's that for a trade-last?"

Dan weighed this compliment with a twinkle in his eye. "Lucky I didn't model a pig, or the competition would've been tight."

"Oh, you!" Annie pursed her red lips. "Now what's mine?"

"I don't know whether I ought to tell you or not. Shall I, Cy?"

"Most certainly not. That was a confidence."

"You promised," Annie said.

"Now I've got myself in a box," Dan said.

"You have to tell me," Annie protested.

"If you do, I'll break your neck," Cy threatened.

"You see, Annie? You wouldn't want my neck broken."

"If you don't, I'll never speak to you again!" Annie cried hotly.

"Well, stand between me and Cy and I'll tell you," Dan said. "Cy confided to me that you're the one girl in Concord he minds saying goodbye to most."

Cy started around Annie in an effort to get at Dan.

"Stop it!" Annie begged them and grasped Cy's arm. "Are you going away for a visit, Cy?"

"More than a visit, I'm afraid," Cy sounded doleful. "I'm leaving Concord. Going West."

"But not to live!" Annie exclaimed, for Cy was one of the best catches in town—good family, well-to-do, and very much a man.

"I hope I'll live," Cy said, a reply which made Dan utter a strangled sound.

"But you can't leave Concord!" Annie was shocked. "When do you go?"

"Tomorrow morning. But I don't want anyone to see me off," Cy was managing to sound sadder and sadder.

"But Cy!" This was the point when real emotion had begun to come into all the girls' voices. "You'll have time to stop in this evening? Mother and Father would like to say goodbye."

"I'm afraid you'll have to say it for me, Annie."

"That wouldn't be the same at all."

Dan could contain himself no longer. Annie stared at the youth wondering if extreme amusement was the way one showed acute sorrow. Then the deception dawned on her, and Annie grew pink in the face, then pinker. They had made a fool of her. "I might have guessed!" she cried, half way between anger and mirth at the sight of them. "The two biggest donkeys in Concord! Well, don't expect me to shed any tears at your going, Cyrus Hubbard!"

"I'm shedding them, enough for both," Dan wiped his eyes.

Annie wheeled on Dan. "I've a mind to tell you what one farmer said about your old hound, though I wasn't going to. He said, 'Wa'l, it do look consid'rable like a dog.' So there!"

"Don't go 'way mad, Annie," Dan begged. "Here comes Eva Whalen. Cy hasn't said goodbye to her yet."

"Please," Cy added. "These farewells are very touching."

"I wouldn't be seen in such company!" Annie said, trying to hide her amusement, and walked off.

Dan drew a long breath and said, "Maybe you will have

82

to leave town for keeps, Cy. That's six mortal enemies you've made."

"They'll be down at the station nevertheless," Cy said confidently. "Anyway, I'm only doing it so you'll have to come with me."

"Last year I might've, but not this."

Fanny Hubbard came running up. "Oh, Dan! The premiums have just been posted. You've won $3 for your owls!"

"I see what you mean!" Cy smiled.

Fame begins in unnoticeable ways—the first breath of praise is repeated, then circulated through one town and into the next town, into the borough, the county, and finally it spreads throughout the state. Praise becomes a reputation which widens, deepens, stretches out more, until what was once a few idle words is a glory that reaches the final shining peak of fame—immortality.

Dan was at last noticed, and it was that Cattle Show that informed Concord of his existence. "A nice chap, yes. Does well with his strawberries, and is very well liked, I hear, but I didn't know he made those what-do-you-call-them figures. That hound dog of his; the very spit an' image of our Bruce. And the owls! Did you see those love birds? Quite a notion. Mattie talked about them all the way home. As for me, the hound was more to my taste. He's got quite a knack, I should say. What's his name again? Dan'l French?"

Dan was invited to the Cambridge Assembly and was more favorably received than any other youth.

Impressed by the Cattle Show premium, Uncle Simon Brown wrote a puff about his nephew in the *Boston Journal*.

Mrs. Ralph Waldo Emerson, meeting Pamela shopping on the Mill Dam, requested Dan's presence at a sit-down tea that night at six.

"Oh, Dan!" Pamela cried after dinner. "You'll never for-

83

give me. You were invited to the Emersons' for supper! How terrible!"

Judge French looked up from his paper. "It's fortunate that Emerson is a philosopher, my dear."

"Yes, but Mrs. Emerson may not be one."

"I'll go now," Dan said. "They sit up pretty late."

Hitching Stubtail, he drove off to the white house on Lexington Road, a house that managed to look as benign and yet as reserved as its owner.

Dan had been invited here before, but with the family never by himself. To be asked in for an evening by the frail sixty-eight-year-old Emerson, inundated by callers from all over the world, was a great honor.

The tall figure coming to the post office for his mail like anyone else reminded Dan of Dante in the book Sallie had given him. He wore a long black cloak like a shawl, Dante-fashion, and his presence brought serenity.

Dan hitched the horse and walked up the path to the house standing in the moonlight. A shadow scampered to the door ahead of him—a kitten. He knocked and picked the animal up, and found he was still holding the purring creature after he had made his excuses and Mr. and Mrs. Emerson had put him at his ease.

"By the way, this is your kitten not mine," Dan said.

"Oh, dear, they'll be the death of me!" replied Mrs. Emerson.

"You seem to be the death of them first," Mr. Emerson smiled. "Tell Dan about last night."

"You can tell him while I fetch some pears."

The story did not surprise Dan. Mrs. Emerson could not bear to drown kittens, of which there was always an over-supply, without chloroforming them first. Last night a badly injured kitten had to be put out of pain but there was no chloroform. So Mrs. Emerson dressed, went to the drugstore, found it closed, walked to the druggist half a mile out Lowell Road, got him out of bed—for no one could refuse an Emerson—and finally Mrs. Emerson was able to see that the poor creature was put out of its misery.

Dan's practical mind calculated that the kitten had suffered two hours longer than necessary so that Mrs. Emerson could spare her sensibilities, but did not mention it. A saint had difficulties enough.

Mr. Emerson brought out a collection of pictures of statues from abroad. He insisted that Dan sit in a chair before a large magnifying glass, while he stood and named them.

Mrs. Emerson came back with the fruit. "It pleases us very much, Dan, that you are interested in sculpture. Concord has never had anyone to develop our perceptions in that line. Tell us, if you care to, whether you have plans for more education."

Dan mentioned that he hoped to study under Mr. Ward of New York.

"I'm glad to hear that," Mr. Emerson said. "Progress in living is much like going up a ladder. Each step requires its special effort but also gives a grander view."

"It's choosing which step to take next that I find hard," Dan said.

"In a ladder the next step is always immediately in front."

"That's so," Dan assented. "And when I do take the step right in front, I get along all right."

Mr. Emerson's clear eyes regarded his young visitor with favor. "You're fortunate, Dan, to have found that out. And this will happen so often that you may know it is not simply chance. There *is* divine assistance. And wisdom begins when a man lets things happen through him. It's a little like steering a boat. Once you're well set in your course, the less you meddle with the tiller, the straighter you go."

"Indeed," said Mrs. Emerson quietly, "I should not call a man great until he is accomplishing more than he could do with only his own strength."

Dan felt as though a fire had been built under his heart. This lean man, whose hands and feet were too large for his small head, but whose mind had so much wisdom, was taking him into his inner circle. The scholar who typified the very best of America had seen something in him, Dan French, and was trying to encourage him. He would always remember this evening and the deep full voice, now commenting on some foreign marble, now telling some simple story, now phrasing some truth in a way that was memorable forever.

When it came time to jog home behind Stubtail, with the leafless elms wearing hoods of moonlight and the night stillness like an extension of the wordless benediction he had received, Dan knew he had been reinforced. He felt his powers unlimited. Mr. Emerson had given him a boost up the ladder.

He hated to go to bed.

At last Dan had a studio of his own. The town had rented him a room in the Town Hall, and half the girls in town had helped him fix it up as work-room, complete with guest-book and skeleton.

"Why the skeleton?" asked Sallie, when he had taken his family to see his arrangements.

"Yes, I've heard of a death's head at a feast," said Judge French, "but never the whole skeleton."

"She's my hostess," Dan grinned. "You'd be surprised how a few bones hanging up loosen the tongue-tied. Judge Hoar brought Judge Gray in yesterday and she was the first thing that caught their eyes."

86

"She?" the Judge's eyebrows went up. "It looks to me remarkably like an it."

"Oh, Father!" Sallie groaned. "Please let Dan have her as his adored one. Then mother won't have to worry."

All laughed but Pamela, whose attention was taken by a new Dickens group Dan was working on—Dolly Varden and Joe Willett. It was a charming thing. Lucy Barrett had posed for Dolly in a costume which she had made and which Dickens would have approved. The effect was flirtatious enough to please a monk.

"It's perfect, Dan!" Sallie cried. "Even to the way she holds her hands."

"I had endless trouble with them," Dan said. "Yesterday Lucy saw that they worried me and said, 'Why don't you fix them this way,' and her hands fell into the most coquettish position imaginable. As you can see."

"That did not give Lucy endless trouble," the Judge remarked and Sallie laughed. Pamela still said nothing and did not laugh.

"Don't you think it's cute, Mother?" Sallie asked.

"I'm afraid I do," Pamela said.

Dan flinched almost visibly at the chill of his stepmother's criticism. She had been so warmly enthusiastic over his efforts so far that this rebuke hurt. "What's wrong?" he asked quietly.

"Nothing," Pamela said. "It's very well done, very pretty. It should sell, too. It's as sentimental as one of these Rogers groups you see in every home."

"Mother, please don't be cryptic!" Sallie implored.

"People don't want plain-speaking," Pamela replied crisply. "Especially in art, or about art. They prefer soothing syrup."

"Pamela, I think you owe it to Dan to be more explicit,"

87

Judge French said. "For what this statue aims to be I think it's excellent."

"So do I," Pamela said emphatically, "for what it aims to be. But is that enough? Is Dan's object to go on doing these sentimental scenes, or to be an artist?"

Dan was trying to forget his hurt and listen, for when Pamela was in the saddle she usually had something of value to say.

"You mean you'd like Dan to do Civil War scenes? Boys being shot and run through with bayonets?" Sallie demanded.

"I cannot dictate to Dan," Pamela said. "His genius will do that."

"You make a good substitute, Mother Pamela," Dan said. "I've been so engrossed in this, I've not stepped back to look it over."

Pamela sounded a little less stiff as she said, "It's in the air, this sort of thing Dan. We've just had such years of the War's awfulness, that we all want to shelter ourselves from even thinking of it. We want roses covering the graves so they can be forgotten. Art must be peaceful, one vast Decoration Day. But if I know anything about art it's not meant to put you to sleep."

"Oh, Mother!" Sallie groaned. "It's as full of fun as—"

"Let her finish, please," Dan said to his sister.

"I have finished," Pamela said. "Complacency is fatal. I think that's what I'm trying to say. Your owls were sentimental, but were saved by their humor, and I thought them very good. But now you do another statue that is sentimental and humorous and make no advance. One or two more successes as a maker of sham sentiment might turn you into a second Mr. Rogers and end your career as an artist. Do you see what I mean?"

88

"Yes," Dan said. His stepmother had certainly seen into his tendency more clearly than he had.

"It's the same danger that Concord is in," Pamela continued. "Concord's like an extinct star. It continues to shine a long time after it has really gone out."

"Pamela, really!" the Judge was amused.

"You'd better not let Concord hear you say so!" Sallie said with a gasp.

"That's precisely the point," Pamela said. "The brilliance of her great era is still so dazzling that she thinks she is still burning with creative flame. It's perfectly natural. The point is that an artist daren't think he can go on doing safely what he has been doing. He must grow." She turned to Dan and said, "Forgive me, Dan. I do believe in you. That's why I say these things."

CHAPTER

11

PAMELA'S WORDS sank deep into Dan. She had uncovered a very real danger. It was strange, Dan thought as he bought his ticket for New York, how honest real people like Patrick and Pamela, could say things that made him so angry yet turned out to be so helpful. One thing, he determined; he was never going to get mad at frank criticism. The very fact that it made you burn up, or want to, was a signal to stop, listen, and consider. They might be telling you something free of charge you ought to hear. Suppose he had told his stepmother to go to grass, however properly; he would be launching out on another sentimental effort instead of seeking an appointment with Mr. Ward for more instruction. He had vaguely intended to seek out Mr. Ward, who was certainly the best sculptor in the East, but Pamela had provided the needed shove.

By a curious coincidence, his Aunt Catherine Welles in Brooklyn had provided a pull. She had seen a copy of Dan's owls in a New York dealer's shop and had bought them not knowing the sculptor.

"And to think it was one of the family!" she had written

90

Dan. "Do come pay us a visit so that we can get acquainted with our gifted nephew."

It was convenient, Dan thought on the train, to have relatives stationed in such places as he wished to visit. And he was happily surprised by the quiet luxury of the Welles dwelling. Doctoring must pay. Most interesting to him were the pictures; Italian primitives, he was told. These religious painters didn't mind getting in a rut, Dan thought, and wondered what Pamela would have said to them.

His aunt had pulled strings to induce Mr. J. Q. A. Ward to receive Dan. The noted sculptor had not agreed to accept Dan as a pupil, but consented to look at his drawings.

"He doesn't look like a sculptor at all," Mrs. Welles said. "More like a prize fighter. I really expected to see him in tights and gloves with cauliflower ears."

"That's good. The classes I've attended have been mostly girls, as if sculpturing was hardly a man's business."

"Well, don't let him knock you out in the first round," Doctor Welles said, as Dan started off for Mr. Ward's studio near Central Park. Dan had decided to walk the five miles in order to get into athletic condition, as he put it, before meeting this human buffalo.

One glance at the big studio told Dan that Mr. Ward did not need money and would not wish to squander time on a beginner. The man himself was thick-chested, strong-voiced, in the prime of life. His handshake was reassuring. The last suspicion of effeminacy in his lifework fled from Dan's mind.

Mr. Ward took the portfolio of Dan's drawings over to a desk to study, leaving Dan to stare at the studio. An impartial radiance from a large skylight bathed the room. Plaster casts stood like milestones of work done. Statuary on the way to completion indicated that Mr. Ward could work on several commissions at once. In the rear stood a replica of "The Indian Hunter" which New York City had set up in Central Park.

Glancing from this statue tingling with restrained masculinity and alert poise—to its sculptor, Dan was struck by the resemblance of work and maker. Not that the redskin resembled Mr. Ward—they were a civilization apart. But Dan's quick eye had detected the equation under the surface. Temperamentally they were of a piece. By sheer creative force the sculptor had said, "Be this!" to his clay and the finished figure answered, "I am."

This authenticity of cause and effect thrilled Dan. It was all positive, genuine, without trick or sentimentality. The figure displayed the proper passion of its nature—and that sufficed. In that illuminated moment Dan took leave of all his past work. The owls and the Dolly Varden were toys. He had become a man, and he resolved henceforth to show what he saw, what he felt, without an ounce of prettification.

Mr. Ward called him over. Dan was apprehensive. He saw now that he had drawn the very things that Mr. Ward did not like and did not do. The sculptor shoved the drawings aside, confirming Dan's fears and said, "I've declined pupils for some time now. I am simply too busy, Mr. French. But if you care to come here and work in my studio for a month, I'll keep an eye on you. The charge will be $50."

"Thank you," Dan said. "I can learn a lot in a month."

Mr. Ward stood up. "Come as early as you like tomorrow. I have an engagement or I'd have you start today."

"May I ask if it is Aunt Catherine Welles or the drawings that did this?" Dan smiled in relief.

"You may be sure that if I hadn't liked the drawings, I'd have declined you."

"But they're so different from what you go in for, sir."

"What difference does that make? Do you think I want you to stand on my feet?"

Dan knew he could persist with this forthright artist. "You aren't telling me why you make an exception for me, sir."

The sculptor smiled slightly. "The thing was you, of course," he said gruffly. "What else is there to build on? These drawings aren't the whole of you, I may hope. Certainly not the best of you. But they aren't mere copying. Look," and he pointed at a tub of clay he was about to use, "that hundred pounds of clay holds my secret. It also holds your secret, and a hundred other secrets. It's neutral. It doesn't even wish you well. It is simply opportunity made visible. The rest is up to you—your honesty, your utter faithfulness to what you see. That's what the first necessity of the sculptor is—integrity of eye and desire. I can help you realize your insight. I can give you the few universals of technique which all sculptors have found necessary. But I can't give you the desire to be honest, the passionate hunger to bring out of that clay the statue you're capable of seeing in it."

"I see," Dan said, thankful he had drawn as he saw.

"Good. We shall get on together," answered Mr. Ward.

During the next month Dan discovered what it was to work. The long hours of modeling in his corner of the studio, the endeavor to salt down all he was being told, watching Mr. Ward cast a figure, were strenuous enough. Mr. Ward had other suggestions. The Academy of Design offered free instruction on Monday, Wednesday, and Friday nights, which Dan took advantage of.

Fortunately he was strong as a lithe ox. Thanks to his father's precept and example, his choice of friends, a certain inner fastidiousness of nature, and the fact that his hours were filled with activity, Dan had easily put aside any temptations to dissipation. So now freedom from parental watch-

93

fulness made no change in his behavior, and he underwent the punishing routine without flinching.

As a graduation test, Mr. Ward had Dan choose his own subject to model. Dan had been yearning to visit the circus which was setting up its tents in Brooklyn. Deciding to combine both pleasure and business—a secret blend of enjoyment he had discovered as a boy—he suggested a group of lions.

Mr. Ward laughed, "You don't mind going in over your head, do you!"

"I'm used to lions," Dan said with a smile. "My brother and I did some once in snow, and that week there weren't any better lions in all of Cambridge." Dan did not add that lions were a subject far removed from the sentimental subjects he had determined to relinquish.

"All right, go ahead with it," the sculptor said. "It's a good sign to be fascinated by the difficult. Easy pulls you down. Difficult tries to lift you up."

So Dan took his drawing board to the circus and before the crowd arrived, asked permission to sketch the king and queen of beasts.

Circus hands are obliging people and they assisted heartily. The trainers and the trapeze artists, the girls who pirouetted on horseback and the clowns, watched with whispered amazement as this young man transferred to paper the lions' sinuosities and powerful grace. When a shower started and a fine rain drizzled through the canvas, the dare-devil who jumped through blazing hoops offered to hold an umbrella over Dan. The manager proposed to get the lions in any position Dan wanted.

"Ain't that a wonder!" said a lean wrinkled woman in a ballet costume. "Look 't the General's head, if it ain't his spit 'n' likeness!"

94

"General who?" Dan asked.

"General Grant, and don't he look like him too!"

"The lioness is Mrs. Grant then?"

"Sakes no!" the sinewy old woman laughed shrilly. "You'd make a fine circus man! *She's* Cleopatra. We got to name the beasts for people in the public eye, or they wouldn't look at 'em."

Dan laughed and wondered if Cleopatra was more in the public eye than the President's wife. Probably the circus instinct was right.

Back at the studio he made his complicated armatures without help. As he modeled, he had no trouble remembering the feline majesty of his subjects. Yet when he asked for the verdict he was not certain of approval.

Mr. Ward studied the group a long while. He looked far more formidable to Dan than any lion.

At length he said, "You've got it—the main thing. That is lion. You've got the burden of lion nature that lions have to bear."

"I'm not sure I tried to," Dan said modestly.

"It's there, just the same. You have to get the subject's point of view. For instance, if you're doing a figure of a child looking at his toes, you know what's passing through his mind—admiration, curiosity, delight that they wiggle when he wants them to. You can choose only one mood, so you aim for one that's both typical and unique. The great statues are done when the sculptor is sympathetic with his subject's greatest moment and has caught it so plainly that the onlooker feels convinced."

"Do you think I've got away from the sentimental?"

"Completely," Mr. Ward said to Dan's utter relief. "Your owls were a travesty on owlhood—intentionally, of course. But these lions convey their lionhood, all that innate power and latent ferocity we humans secretly envy."

95

"They look pretty raw yet."

"Naturally. One does not turn out finished works of art in a few days. You got the first thing first, which is what I wanted to see. I can tell whether a pupil has promise simply by watching his attitude towards detail. If he's too neat and careful at the start the chance is he'll never see the whole in his mind's eye. Get the construction right before you decorate. What are you going to do when you get back to Concord?"

"Throw everything I've done out of the window."

"And then?"

"I don't know," and suddenly Dan recalled his birthday party when he had given the same answer to his Aunt Ann about his lifework. Yet things had worked out. "You'll probably think it's funny," he said to Mr. Ward, "but things work out best for me when I let them come."

"Sounds like Micawber to me. If it's only walking across a room, you've got to know where you're heading or you bump into a wall."

"What would you suggest?" Dan asked lamely.

"Something you have to reach for," the sculptor said. "Your instinct was right about tackling those lions. Earn your money by commissions, busts, anything. You've got to be self-supporting to keep your self-respect, at any rate in our mode of civilization. But you should be on the lookout for this big thing that will pull you ahead. It must appeal to you so tremendously that you'll throw your whole energy and devotion into it."

"Do you think I should come to New York?"

"Not a bit of it. An artist is strongest when standing on his own soil."

"You've given me a real start," Dan said.

"I'm much pleased with the results of your month here. Come see me when you're in town again."

The train ride back to Boston was all exaltation. He would do something big, really BIG, if only to justify Mr. Ward's faith in him. This was a vow between himself and himself, between the Dan French that others saw and the Dan French *he* knew he was—and could be.

The rainbow ride lacked particulars. It was all rosy dream and easy glow, and it lost some of its color in the tiresome details of changing from station to station, missing his supper, and arriving late on foot carrying his valise.

But the glow kindled again at Pamela's kiss and Sallie's hug and his father's gladness at seeing him back. Cold chicken and hot tea were quickly assembled, and the family sat around him as he ate asking questions which he answered between mouthfuls of food.

Nor was the news all one way. During his absence Mr. Monroe had announced that he was going to give Concord a library in keeping with its literary preeminence. And Annie Keyes was engaged to be married to Edward Emerson.

"So we are going to be related to the Sage of Concord!" Dan commented. "That ought to help."

Also a committee had been formed to celebrate the Centennial of the Concord Fight in 1775.

"They're starting early enough," Dan commented. "That's years off." He picked up his dishes and carried them into the kitchen, and then picked up his hat.

"Don't tell me you're going to forsake us already!" Pamela cried.

"Dan has a natural curiosity to see where else he's been missed," Judge French interpreted.

"I can tell him that!" Sallie said tartly. "Lucy is not wearing black exactly and, for *second* best, seems to be doing very well with Fred Denny."

"Thanks for the tip," Dan said quickly. "It's time I was

97

back." At the door he remembered what he wanted to ask. "Were you put on the Centennial Committee, Father?"

"You honor me, Son. The Honorable John Keyes is chairman and the other two members are no less than Mr. Emerson and Judge Hoar."

"Cousin John, eh?" Dan's smile widened. "Well, maybe he can get us front seats at the parade."

CHAPTER

12

DAN WAS off to pay his duty call on Annie Keyes.
He was in a divided state of mind. In the three days
since reaching home from New York, he had already settled
deep into the old happy rut. He had helped his father make
a cow-pen, had been chosen director of the next ball to be
given by the Young Men's Club, had been invited to be
usher at Charlie Baird's wedding, was told that he had been
put on the Decoration Day Committee, and had spent this
morning helping Pamela turn the parlor carpet, which he
had beaten dustless on the lawn. It was delightful, but no
one had offered him a commission, and no idea for a world-
startling statue had come to mind.

He turned Stubtail into the Keyes' driveway. From the
number of carriages around they must be having a party,
Dan thought. All the better.

Concord fashion he walked right in. One of the best
things about Concord was this feeling of being one big
family under different roofs. The first person he ran into
was John Keyes hanging up his topcoat.

"Greetings, stranger!" The older man shook hands with

his cousin. "Did you have a satisfactory time in New York?"

"Yes, thanks. I put some solid education under my feet."

"The Judge tells me you've taken up sculpture as a life-work. I can't imagine anything more difficult."

"It strikes me that way too, sometimes," Dan smiled.

"I wish you were farther along with your career, Dan," Mr. Keyes said thoughtfully. "Mr. Emerson and I consider a statue erected on Buttrick's Hill a fitting memorial to the men who took up their position there before marching down to the Bridge."

Dan's mind jumped back to his talk with Lucy Barrett that morning he had rowed her to the Bridge. "You mean a statue of one of the men? A Continental Minute Man?"

"Hardly that. I rather fancy a statue of Major Buttrick leading his men. In that pose, I mean. The officer striding ahead with his sword drawn. You've seen statues like that."

Dan had—too many of them.

"Judge Hoar inclines to a statue on the Square. It's true more people would see it."

"Have you considered the Bridge?" Dan asked.

"There's already one monument at the Bridge. I don't believe we need two, Dan," John Keyes looked at the young man thinking what a likeable chap he'd grown to be. "Anyway, we may have to give it up. There seems to be a shortage of sculptors."

"How about me?" Dan wanted to ask, ached to ask, but something held him back. John Keyes had a robust laugh. Besides it was preposterous. He had better hold his tongue.

Yet his mind would not hold *its* tongue. He remembered the sketches of Continentals he had made after that squabble with Lucy. Where were they? He had no idea, and suddenly the necessity of finding them, looking at them, seized him like some physical urge. He groped back into the coat closet and ran for the door. Annie could wait. If those sketches were as appropriate to this new opportunity as he remembered—

The answer made him dizzy. "Idiot!" he said to his mind. But something deeper paid no attention.

"Dan! Dan, you're not going!"

Lucy Barrett reached him, looking her most charming.

"I just thought of something I have to do."

"But not right off!" The girl even managed that Dolly Varden look in her eyes. There was no need to hurry, he told himself.

Then that deeper urge insisted and he opened the door.

"Everybody will be so disappointed!" cried Lucy.

"If you'd left the water running and the stopper in the basin, you'd run wouldn't you?" he asked, looking down at her almost sternly, his dark eyes handsome with life.

"Oh, Dan, is it that?" Her voice instantly filled with concern.

"No, but it's something just as important. Please don't tell anyone you've seen me."

He let himself out, carried along by this inner necessity. Nothing had taken hold of him so powerfully as the anxiety to see those sketches. As Stubtail hurried indignantly, he reviewed the places where he had hidden them. Then it came to him. He had moved some of his things into that studio he'd made under the skylight. But Pamela had said something about having straightened it up. His heart sank. When Pamela straightened a place up, there was nothing left to straighten. Pamela did not believe in attics, midden heaps, the fossilizing remains of generations. The furnace, she thought, was man's finest invention.

He tied up Stubtail and burst into the studio. The worst had happened. It was as clean and neat as a dog's set of teeth. For a moment he hated his stepmother and all meddling women. And then he remembered and tore up to his room.

The bottom drawer of his chest of drawers was locked, safe, unrifled. He opened it and there lay the portfolio marked "Private—UNDERSTAND?"

And all this fuss for nothing! All this leaving Lucy and lathering Stubtail. The sketches were ludicrous—stiff, trite. Only one was worth looking at a second time. In this he had tried to work a plow into the picture to show that the man was a farmer. The minute man was stooping to pick up his musket. It was impossible, of course, yet it did have a realistic quality. But too disjointed. You couldn't have a man here, a plow there.

Dan propped this sketch against his pillow and studied it. The first depression caused by his thwarted eagerness was wearing off. The minute man was a good subject. He didn't have to be stooping. The musket could be leaning against the plow or a rock. That was a detail. As Mr. Ward said, get your main objective first.

Then depression came on him again. The town would have to pass on this enterprise. He could imagine some common-sense citizen rising in town meeting and saying, "Is the chairman actually proposing that the town entrust this important work to an inexperienced youth who has never made a statue?" The howls of mirth! The unanimous vote of no! And who was to persuade Mr. Keyes to make such a proposal in the first place?

Yet he continued to look at his figure. It had life. And meaning. How could he give it up?

The question tossed him, hazed him. In the blessed solitude of his room, he thought until he was exhausted. He knew he had to try. Let them call him a conceited idiot, he had to try. Mr. Emerson would understand. He was the one to see. And first he must get this Continental in the right pose and take that to Mr. Emerson. He would at least look at it with sympathetic eyes. "Nothing ventured, nothing gained." He had always advocated the great venture; now Dan would see if he would back it up.

By suppertime Dan had fortified himself behind his resolve.

"What became of you?" Sallie demanded at the table. "Mr. Keyes said you were there but nobody saw you."

"Did he tell you that he'd just commissioned me to do a statue of a Continental Minute Man for the Centennial?"

"No, strangely enough, he didn't!" Sallie was not taken in.

"Well, I shouldn't be surprised if he did," Dan said. He was conscious of his father and mother looking at him.

"What are you talking about?" Pamela asked.

Dan repeated the talk he had had with Mr. John Keyes, and mentioned the sketches he had made, announcing that he was seriously going to try for a commission.

"But do you think you can?" Pamela exclaimed, startled by the idea and not helped much by Dan's casualness.

"If he can't, I can show him!" Judge French said.

"Oh, Father!" Sallie cried. "This is serious."

"So am I," Judge French concurred. "The idea is sound. What could be more fitting than a statue of the farmer who made all the trouble."

"But wouldn't it be wonderful!" Pamela exclaimed. "Dan, go get the sketches won't you?"

Dan shook his head. "I want to do a lot to them before I show anybody. And please, don't say a word to anybody. I want to try out all sorts of poses and combinations before I show any model at all."

"Very sensible," the Judge said, and they all promised absolute secrecy.

Under his composure, the Judge was excited. That evening alone with his wife, he said, "This is worth our long wait, Pamela."

103

"But do you believe it possible?" Pamela had always looked at things so practically that this enormous ambition was overwhelming. "This is for the world to see, Henry, and Dan is so young."

"Young, but deeper than we thought, and courageous. I almost dare hope that Emerson will back him up in it."

"Mr. Emerson, yes. But Judge Hoar, no. And there's the town. Can you fancy them commissioning this child to make a monument of such importance to Concord?"

"Don't put hurdles in his way, Pamela."

"I'm not. I'm as eager for him to try it as you are."

"Then cease thinking of him as a child. Hasn't he shown himself mature in seeing this opportunity and bravely grasping it? It makes me proud. I declare I don't know when I've been so moved."

CHAPTER

13

DURING THE next days of work, Dan was cut off from all interests but one—the creation of a statue so compelling that the Committee must accept it. His eagerness of concentration sealed off all other thoughts and gave the right of way to ideas that would bring forth the final and right conception. It did a hundred things to his imagination, loosened it, directed it.

Effects began to show. Three constants were kept in each sketch—the young farmer, the plow, and the musket. His problem was to join plow and man into one flowing whole. The plow stuck out. He experimented with a farm horse instead, but it seemed to detract from the man. What, he asked himself, must be the main interest?

This question haunted him. He was artist enough to know that this central idea must be thought out clearly or else he would waste time and clay indefinitely. And time was important. Even now the Committee might be inviting some other sculptor to do this memorial.

He stopped drawing and started to make small clay models —five or six inches high—embodying the main elements of his shifting ideas. What did Concord want to see in this statue? A bronze figure lasted for centuries. Only an idea of the most compelling interest could invite looking at time and time again. What was the idea behind the Minute Man? Duty? Impatience at having his life interrupted? Courage? Anger over tyranny? What did that morning of April 19, 1775, *mean*?

Dan's fingers did not tell him. They were concerned with detail. Only his mind could tell. He took the question to bed with him. The problem woke him in the black of night, and he would fall asleep more often discouraged than inspired. Should the farmer be starting to run? Should he peer ahead—no, that was imitating the *Indian Hunter*. Should he be alert as if he had just heard gun-shots?

Trying to get back to the feel of that day, Dan placed a chair as plow and posed himself. It was hot, history said, summer-hot though mid-April. Therefore the farmer would not be wearing a coat, though he might have it with him. The coat was really essential. But how depict it? On the ground? No drama in that. Taking it off? No one could look at that without smiling. Throw it over the plow handle? Perhaps. Drat the coat! Perhaps the farmer's rolled up sleeves could indicate the season.

The clay statuettes multiplied. Dan filled his mantel with them, then the bureau, the window-ledge, with moist cloths over each to keep the clay manageable.

"It doesn't smell healthy!" Pamela complained. "Minnie can't sweep. She can't even make the bed."

"Please tell Minnie to keep out," Dan said.

"It can't be wise to sleep in such an atmosphere," Pamela objected.

"It's not half as damp as a foggy day and I've lived through several of them."

"I've an idea, Dan. Why not move your work to Will's

room? We can take up the matting and I'll have Patrick store the furniture somewhere."

"I wish I got inspirations like that!" Dan laughed his relief. Will's room was just right, on the ground floor, nearer water, and away from the harassed maid Minnie.

"How is your Continental coming along, dear?"

"I've bred nearly a regiment," Dan said. "But I haven't yet hit the right combination. The plow gets in my road. The farmer isn't one thing or the other. When I think 'farmer' he's not military enough, and when I think 'soldier' he's no farmer. Also he's too amiable. This fellow cursed to high heaven when the British pulled him away from his potato-patch. Yet if I make him scowl, he's unpleasant."

"Well, you'll get it," Pamela said confidently. "If you have an idea, there certainly is a way to express it. I'll tell Patrick about the furniture."

"I'll tell him. In fact I'll help him," Dan said. "I've hardly moved out of this house for days."

"All right. And do you mind carrying that ladder under the elm back to the shed?"

Dan obliged, never dreaming he was walking into a trap. But as he reached the elm, Florence Gillson appeared—a shrewd, gifted, thinnish girl with an over-developed critical faculty. Florence might have stood fifteenth on his list; he was, he feared, close to first on hers.

"Abou ben Adhem!" she greeted him.

"May his tribe increase!" Dan replied as he was supposed to. He was getting up tableaux based on the story of Abou ben Adhem, and Florence was cast as the Recording Angel. Dan had experienced much inward mirth at making Florence the chronicler of the sins and virtues of those around her. She would not have to stir an inch out of her usual role.

"Where have you been since you got back from New York?"

107

"A man has to work for his living."

"But not day *and* night."

Dan shifted to the attack. "Have you got the angels picked out yet?"

"Yes. Can't we sit down on your step and talk?"

"I have to do an errand for mother right away," Dan said. "I'll look you up very soon. Who are the angels? Beth Hoar's one, I suppose," he added mischievously, knowing that Florence had an abiding jealousy of the reigning social princess.

"No, Beth is too stately for an angel," Florence said. "And angels are supposed to be thinking of someone besides themselves."

"Miaow!" Dan mewed.

"I'm not being catty, Dan," Florence said. "Nobody admires Beth more than I do, but you have to look at people as they are when you're picking them for a play."

"Well, you chose Lucy Barrett I hope," Dan said with a delicacy of malice that amused him to his little toe.

"Oh, no, Dan!" Florence replied seriously. "Lucy's too cute. Angels aren't cute, you know."

"No, I've never met one," Dan said. "How about Jeannie Richardson?"

Florence shook her head. "You know that she and I don't get on well together, Dan. We have very different ideas about everything."

"Well, who did you choose?"

Florence named her friends. It interested him that she had left every one of his friends out of the cast. Girls were riddles. Maybe that was the secret that bothered the Sphinx. He picked up the ladder. "I think I've solved the way to fade the angels out, Florence. With gauze. You start with ten thicknesses, say, and remove one thickness when the light shifts, making the angel plainer and plainer."

"It sounds like a lot of trouble."

108

"But it looks like a miracle. We'll talk about it. Now I've got to run."

"I wish we *could* talk!" Florence said. "I've something I think you should be told—for your own good."

"Save it," Dan called over his shoulder.

Patrick and Dan transferred the furniture at once and there was still twenty minutes before Patrick went home to dinner.

"Do something for me, Patrick?" Dan asked. "I want you to be a Continental Minute Man for a moment." He picked up a horse-blanket. "Do you mind coming out to the plow?"

Patrick followed, good-naturedly. "I've been most everything else in me life, so I might as well be a statue. Now what?"

"This is the situation," Dan said. "You're plowing. It was chilly early, so you brought a coat. You know you're likely to be summoned any minute, so you brought your musket." He handed Patrick the blanket and a stick. "You've just heard the signal telling you the British are coming. What're you going to do about it?"

"You asking an Irishman that?" Patrick said. "I'd do the natural thing. I'd go for 'em."

"Let's see you do it."

For ten minutes Patrick rehearsed the call to arms and Dan watched, saying nothing. Finally Dan called a halt and thanked his model.

"I don't know what you're thankin' me for," Patrick said mopping his brow.

"You've given me some ideas."

"It's kind of a long-drawn out thing, ain't it," Patrick remarked. "Like scatterin' corn to the hens and hopin' for an egg."

Dan smiled. "I wish it was as sure as that," he said.

109

After supper two days later, the family sat in conclave with Dan as showman. He had picked out four models, one of which he wanted the judges to choose as best. But he was stating no preference. He had even tossed up a coin to see in what order the little groups were to be shown.

For the first exhibit he brought in a clay model that he knew Sallie would like. The minute man had heard the call and was standing bareheaded with the musket across his body. He was too romantically alert for Dan, but would do as a foil for the more realistic farmer of his choice.

The family, by request, had kept out of Will's room, and were amazed at the jump ahead Dan had made over anything they had seen.

"Oh, that's it!" Sallie cried. "Isn't he *glorious!*"

The Judge said that he was going to maintain a judicial silence until he had seen the four. Pamela said, "I like it, Dan, very much."

Dan brought in the next model, his favorite, with an unemotional, "Here's the next." In this case the plow gave balance to the figure, yet he had got it out of the road. His minute-youth had turned his back on it, though with his left hand still on the handle, while the right hand grasped the musket half-way up. The blessed coat had fallen over the brace between the handles of the plow. The farmer was hatted and looking up alertly, defiantly but without swagger.

Dan waited for some response. No one said a word, and his great hope turned to bitterness. They didn't like it, he said to himself. Then the Judge broke the silence. "Son!" he said, very much moved.

"It's marvellous!" Pamela cried. "It's amazingly all one piece. How did you ever do it?"

"Patrick sweated for it," Dan said.

He looked at Sallie. "I don't think it's as *pretty* as the other," she said.

"Thank goodness!" the Judge said, breaking his vow. "We're not concerned with prettiness. This man's alive. He's strong. Every line of him—his flintlock, coat, and plow, give out the one grand expression of resolution. I have a feeling, Dan, that there's your statue."

Dan's spirits leaped, but he concealed how much he was touched by this praise. Out of his never-failing store of mischief, he even brought in the third model with a "Now here is really something."

"No, no, the other is immeasurably better," said his father.

The same verdict was given the fourth. To be safe, Dan brought in some of the discarded models. But nothing approached the second statue.

Dan looked at the clock. "I want to show this to Mr. Emerson," he said.

"Tonight? It's after eight, dear," Pamela objected.

"Dan's right. He should lose no time. It's been preying on my mind that he might be too late," said his father. "Would you like me to go along?"

"I'd like it very much, but it might smack of pressure," Dan said. "I think it'd make more impression on the author of 'Self-Reliance,' if I went alone."

His father agreed. "I hope the author of 'Compensation' remembers what he wrote."

Dan's lips parted in his happiest grin, and then he disappeared to pack up his model.

THE COLD was so intense that Dan decided to walk to the Emersons' rather than take out Stubtail. The round moon was rising as he turned into Lexington Road at the Tavern corner. This was the first time that Dan had gone to ask a favor in the white house that was a court of greatness for thirty years.

While Dan was not nervous, he was aware of the seriousness of his errand. Mr. Emerson was magnanimous, gentle, considerate. His integrity, however, was solid as marble and could be as cold. Dan was approaching him to be judged and he knew that no bribe of friendliness would influence the philosopher's judgment.

Mrs. Emerson opened the door, since it was the maid's night out. Dan greeted her and asked if Mr. Emerson was in.

After only the slightest hesitation Mrs. Emerson said, "Yes, he is. Come in. This cold is like a wild beast waiting for you."

Dan heard voices. "If he's busy I can come again."

Mrs. Emerson glanced at the covered object in Dan's hand. "You came on a special errand, didn't you Dan? Gossip has good lungs in this town."

Dan smiled. "I'll have to speak to mother about this."

"Oh, I can exonerate her! Your Minnie talks to my Dorothy and so Concord is spared the expense of a town-crier. May I see him?"

Dan laughed and uncovered his model, glad to hear what this woman of intellect and gentleness would say.

"Oh, Dan!" Her exclamation was warm with genuine surprise. "You did this!"

It was, he thought, a funny thing to say. The warm light from the sitting-room fire played on his farmer-warrior. He could see Mrs. Emerson's intense preoccupation with his work and this allayed some of his uneasiness. If it had not impressed her, she could have got through looking at it minutes ago.

"They must see this!" Lidian Emerson said abruptly. "I must tell you, Dan, that Judge Hoar and Mr. Keyes are in Mr. Emerson's study discussing the Centennial. The Judge has heard of a sculptor in New York . . . excuse me a moment."

Anxiety returned to Dan with redoubled power. If Judge Hoar, the acknowledged practical leader of the town, had found a professional sculptor to carry out their wishes, his amateur endeavors had been wasted.

Then Mr. Emerson appeared in the doorway. In spite of the piercing eyes, his thin face looked tired. Removing a fern from a mahogany pedestal, Mrs. Emerson placed the model on it beneath the light. Dan saw with pride that his Continental could stand any illumination. The suspense grew unbearable. Standing beside the philosopher, Dan felt it was impossible to forget Mr. Emerson's fame—although his wife had made him so much at home—and the fact that his model was being scrutinized by the greatest mind in America.

113

Dan glanced from the stately Lidian to those eagle-like eyes. This was the way you felt, Dan thought, just before you were hanged. Suddenly Mr. Emerson looked from the statue to Dan and said, "That tells the story, Dan. May I borrow this for a few minutes? The Judge has some sculptor up his sleeve and I want to show him what Concord can do."

Dan felt a wave of heat go over him and breathed again. He wished Mr. Emerson would let him hear the discussion but he was saying, "Lidian, perhaps Dan would like some of your gingerbread," which meant he was to stay and wait.

"Some hot chocolate would not go amiss?" Mrs. Emerson asked.

"That's trouble for you," Dan said.

"I know no such word," Mrs. Emerson answered. "Will you put another log on the fire and see that it doesn't spark?"

Dan did and sat down to await the next verdict. How was it that his life had become a series of suspenses? Behind the study's closed door, he could hear voices rising in argument and two people speaking at once. Could this aging man of seventy persuade the impressive Judge to reject an experienced sculptor? Could he induce Chairman Keyes to relinquish a statue of Major Buttrick? The Buttricks would have something to say in the final decision.

Mrs. Emerson returned with the chocolate, but even her interest and questions could not conceal the fact that Mr. Emerson and the model were not carrying the committee by storm. The clock said nine fifty-five. Mr. Emerson's "few minutes" had become an hour.

Presently Dan heard Mr. Emerson's step in the hall. His face looked more fatigued than ever. "Be assured, Dan," he said at once. "We have won a point if not the day."

"Oh, Waldo!" Lidian Emerson exclaimed. "I am relieved."

"The consensus of opinion is that we should have a larger

114

replica of this model before expressing a judgment. The town votes upon it, and if the details are brought out more prominently, as they would be in a model thirty inches high, let us say, we should be on surer footing. Could you make such a model before town meeting, Dan?"

In that moment of vast relief Dan would have promised the model in a week. As it was town meeting was a fortnight away. "I'm sure it's possible, sir," Dan said.

"I pledged as much," Mr. Emerson now admitted. "Mr. Keyes and the Judge asked me to convey their congratulations on the model, Dan. Now, if you will excuse me—we are in the midst of decisions."

"Waldo, do send them home!" Mrs. Emerson cried. "You're worn out."

"Not now I'm not." The eagle eyes shone. "But you know Hoar's persistence when he gets a notion."

"Yes, it has made him famous."

Dan gathered that Mr. Emerson had fought for him hard.

It was Dan himself who conceived the wiser course. The idea came to him when he found that he was hurrying, pressed for time. Worry, a new lack of confidence in himself, was waiting at his bedside when he woke. He had trouble making the armature for the larger model. It was no simple matter with a musket and plow to be accounted for as well as the coat and figure. Time was snapping at his heels. He felt as nervous as when he had to take the examinations at Tech.

His inspiration came one gray morning driven with snow when he was harriedly looking at the calendar. "What's the hurry?" he said aloud.

There was no need. It was February, 1873. If the decision was postponed to the November meeting, he would still have nearly a year and a half to make the life-size statue, should they commission him.

The very idea of postponement gave him such a healthy feeling of relief that he began to line up arguments for the Committee. It was dangerous to reopen the subject. But his argument grew more impressive as he tallied the points. He should have time to find specimens of things actually used on that historic morning ninety-eight years ago. What did the flintlock of 1775 actually look like? Who had a powder-horn of the time? And what, for heaven's sake, was the shape of so old-fashioned a plow? Also what kind of leggings? What sort of coat?

Another argument offered. Times were hard. Business firms were failing in Boston. They were going down like ten-pins in New York. His father called it panic. The March town meeting would feel economical. Perhaps times would be better by November. That was risky to bet on, but no riskier than bringing up the subject of an expensive statue now. In November the crops were in and the farmers felt more expansive.

Then, like inspiration itself, the crowning argument came to Dan. It took time to win people to your side. If he worked on the model in a leisurely way through the spring and summer what he was doing would get around. Dan remembered the stir over his little owls at the Cattle Show. Why not put the thirty inch model on display there for all to see? That was the clincher. It was so obvious he wondered why Mr. Keyes or the Judge hadn't thought of it.

Dan felt no trepidation now at carrying his suggestion to the Committee. It was so eminently sensible that they approved at once.

"Since art is long, time should not be fleeting," Mr. Emerson remarked with a smile. "I must have Longfellow amend that line."

With the time-pressure lifted Dan felt that he owned himself again. As the news of the great venture got around, he had encouragement from all sides. His social activities were more extensive than ever.

Lucy Barrett, for all her dimples and chatter, had a downright practical streak and on Dan's behalf set her girl friends going through family attics. The French house took on the look of a museum. A Minute Man costume worn on the famous day by one of the actual participants came to light. He had dressed in a green baize jacket with silver dollars for buttons. Thumbs and fingers had worn the inscriptions on the outer side smooth. His breeches were of tougher stuff, homespun dyed butternut brown, and had shillings for knee-buttons. The long waistcoat must have been awkward to plow in, Dan thought, remembering his attempt. And the upturned hat certainly caught the wind. He was thankful for its jaunty air. That farmer might've worn a cap or tam with disastrous effects to his romantic aspect.

One day, when the roads had dried out, Dan and his father drove over to Acton. They unearthed there the powder-horn used by James Hayward on *the* day. Dan's twenty-third birthday had just passed. He remembered another drive, six years before, right after a birthday. Then he had not known what he was going to be. Now he was deeper in a career than he had dreamt possible. But he was still living on his father.

"This apple's hard to shake," he said apologetically.

"With Sallie getting married next month and Will permanently in Chicago and only an annual visit from Harriette, Pamela and I would be lonely indeed without you, Dan."

"But it's the principle of the thing, as you used to tell me before a spanking," Dan said.

"Your plea is not admitted," the Judge said. "The prin-

117

ciple is this. An artist requires longer to reach maturity than the man of commerce. If he fails in support at the proper time he may never mature. Fortunately I've been in a position to tide you over these beginning years. I see nothing wrong in that from your standpoint and from mine it has been a pleasure and a privilege. And now I am having my reward. This statue, Dan, is going to assist your progress greatly if it is accepted, as I believe it will be. Five or ten years from now you may be earning more than your father."

"That would be a thrill!" Dan nudged Stubtail on. "Do you believe the town will pay me anything beyond expenses if they order the Continental?"

"I think that is a matter best left in abeyance," the Judge said. "At least for the present."

"Mother Pamela doesn't. She says Concord is so obsessed with its importance that it will consider it will have done enough for me by permitting me to work for it."

"Pamela's judgments of Concord are rather extreme," the Judge said. "By the way, you spoke of spanking. I do not remember ever spanking you, sonny."

"That was a figure of speech," Dan said laughing. "But you missed a golden opportunity once."

"How's that?" the Judge was puzzled.

"I was at the wicked age of ten or eleven as I remember," Dan said. "Do you recall those huge Victoria Regina lilies in the Cambridge Botanical Garden?"

"No."

"Don't you even remember hunting up a picture of them in the flower book? They had floating leaves three feet across and had been imported at great expense from Nigeria."

"I have a hazy recollection now. The paper had something about them."

"The paper reported that a gang of hoodlums had wantonly destroyed them, and the Botanical Garden was offering a $50 reward for the dastardly scoundrels. Well, I knew those scoundrels—and so did you. Dick Dana was the other one!"

Judge French looked at his handsome son in amazement.

"You said, 'I'd like to get my hands on those brainless little devils.' You had your arm about me and I was trying not to shiver," Dan laughed again.

"It's coming back to me. Pamela was dreadfully incensed."

"That was the worst of it. Mother Pamela kept saying, 'Why will children do such things!' and you said 'It's because they've not been properly brought up.' And both of you agreed that the House of Correction was too good a place for such toughs and rather favored the jail. I never spent a more uncomfortable morning. I expected the policeman every minute."

"But how could you, even at that age?" the Judge exclaimed. "And young Dana, of all boys!"

"You know what a target, any target is to a wandering youngster, Father. A pebble made a neat round hole. Fifty pebbles made fifty holes, and still the leaves wouldn't sink. Surely you must have noticed how exemplary Dick and I were for days."

"You always *seemed* exemplary," the Judge said with a smile. "Any more confessions?"

"A few," Dan said. "But I think I'll save them."

It was a happy ride and added to the store of affection that each man felt for the other and not for anything would have put into words.

In spite of interruptions, the Minute Man grew with the lengthening days. Defying superstition Sallie wed Ned Bartlett in May. Heat rendered the house unendurable for so great a gathering and the ceremony was performed under a great horse-chestnut tree, causing Dan, who was best man,

119

to remark that this was the first time that a Bartlett pair had been found under a chestnut tree.

"Abou ben Adhem" was a great success under Dan's direction. The device of the appearing and disappearing angels worked to admiration. When one of the cast asked Mr. Emerson if he would like to have the process explained, he replied that he thought he would rather believe it was a miracle.

Dan's rapidly mounting reputation led to great social demands. One such occasion was the June lawn party at Miss Pratt's boarding school for girls. And Dan was asked to give out the prizes.

Immaculate in a new summer suit, Dan entered upon these duties in his usual light-hearted manner. When Mr. Emerson or Mr. Alcott performed this function, there was edification but no laughter. Dan wanted laughter.

So when he was introduced he said, "Good-afternoon, Ladies and Gentlemen. Miss Pratt, as you see, was unable to secure the esteemed service of the Sage of Concord or Mr. Alcott. So who should she call on but the remaining member of Concord's illustrious trio—my most humble self!"

Dan paused and to his horror heard no laughs. Surely they could not dream that he ranked himself with these celebrities.

"Nobody gets a prize until they laugh at that," he said.

This time they laughed. He had saved himself by the skin of his teeth. But it gave him chills up and down his spine. No more humor, he swore to himself. But he could not help it. He told them that he had found out they called him "the plaster-of-Paris boy" and said he was going to speak for three hours before giving a prize. He told them of having learned that they compared notes after dances and had discovered that he had said precisely the same thing to each girl. He told them about the girl who finished her prayers with "please bless papa and mama and please make Worcester the capital of Massachusetts," because that was what she had put on her examination paper. He said that he hoped none of his hearers took advantage of God in that way. They laughed for half an hour, and then when he gave out the prizes he managed to say something charming to each individual who came up. It was undoubtedly as enjoyable a presentation as was ever held on that June lawn.

But it had repercussions for Dan.

He had been rehearsing as the Owl in "Who Killed Cock Robin?" Lightning glimmered through the dusky foliage of great maples along Sudbury Road as he walked home. Florence Gillson, who had not been asked to take part in this play, caught up to him. She had been in the Library and unaware of the storm.

"I'm so thankful I saw you!" she said. "I always feel so *lonely* in a storm."

Big drops began to strike the leaves overhead as they reached the Gillsons'. "Please come in," Florence begged. "You'll get soaked." A sheet of lightning turned her face into a frightened buttercup. "Please do. I'll be scared to death all alone. The family are at Carlisle."

Dan acquiesced, for it seemed a shame to desert the girl. He loved storms and insisted that they sit on the porch.

Suddenly Florence said, "I think it is a friend's duty to be frank, don't you Dan?"

"That depends," Dan said, wondering what was coming.

"Well, I do. I've been meaning to tell you this for a long while, but I never have a chance to see you alone any more, you're so popular."

"What did you want to say?"

"Promise you won't hold it against me, Dan?"

"I never have," Dan said wryly, for he felt sure that Florence was going to give one of her periodic lectures.

121

"It's just this," Florence went on. "I don't blame you for feeling important, Dan. Any man would when he's being flattered all the time. But—and I hate to say this—I'm afraid it's beginning to show."

Thunder drowned Dan's irritated exclamation. Importance was the last thing he felt, especially now when so many obstacles loomed to make him feel extremely humble. But he quickly got control of himself. "So you are worried over my thinking too well of myself, Florence? That it?"

"*I* don't, Dan, but it occurs to me that people who don't know you as well as I do might."

"What have I done now?" asked Dan.

"Well, take the other day at the lawn party—"

"Were you there?"

"No, but I heard about it. Everyone said how much better you were at handing out the prizes than Mr. Alcott or Mr. Emerson. But somebody said she believed you thought so too."

Dan felt his hold on his temper slipping but determined not to let go. "I made an unfortunate joke, Florence, and I learned one important thing. You've got to let a crowd know that you're about to spring a joke or it may miss fire, as mine did. But none of those girls was mad enough to imagine I meant what I said."

"Another thing," Florence went on relentlessly. "You're always crowing about those neckties you win from Lucy at the Cattle Show. When a gentleman defeats a lady, he doesn't rub it in."

"So I'm no gentleman?" Dan was beginning to make a game of this.

"I didn't say that, exactly."

"Well, let me tell you what happens, *exactly*. The whole thing is a joke. Three years ago I bet Lucy a necktie that

122

she couldn't pick the winner in a horse-race, and I won. Next year I won two ties, this year three. If there ever was a gentleman gambler, that's me, for I always allow Lucy to bet *after* the horses start. When a horse gets far ahead and Lucy's sure she has the winner, she bets. Then I choose my nag from the unfortunates she is pleased to leave—and win. It's funny and Lucy tells the joke on herself oftener than I do. Next charge."

"Now you're angry at me!" Florence said.

"How can you think so?" Dan said coolly. "Go ahead, let's get it all cleared up now. What else have I done?"

"I'm sorry I said anything. I'd better be quiet."

"No, Florence. I'm in earnest," Dan said. "Evidently you consider I've been getting too cocky, and I value your opinion sufficiently to explain. Nobody knows how he looks to others, but I think that what you take for an air of importance is hopefulness. I can't help being in good spirits."

"Maybe that's it," said Florence who knew she had gone too far. "You're happy and take no pains to conceal it."

Dan laughed inadvertently. "You think I should look glum?"

"Not glum."

"Remorseful then, for having such a good time?"

"You will twist my words so!" Florence exclaimed. "You know I don't mean that. But everyone's so interested in you and you take it all so *calmly*, as if it were your due!"

"Then I should protest?" Dan was almost enjoying this now, thankful he had kept his temper.

"I give up!" Florence exclaimed. "I'm not going to say another word since you prefer to misunderstand me."

"Please!" Dan begged. "You don't know how much I'm getting out of this. What else did you want to say?"

"Well, if you want to know, I think you have a very funny way of treating girls, Dan. You make each girl think she is the one you care for most of all and . . . and then she finds it isn't so."

A new light was breaking on Dan. He had been avoiding Florence recently because she insisted upon being too possessive while he by his very nature needed to feel free as air. Now her hurt feelings were taking this roundabout way of declaring themselves. Dan, who was genuinely kind, at once felt sorry, though he could not change his nature to accommodate her.

"I don't like cliques, Florence," he said. "And in a small place like Concord, you get the most fun out of knowing everybody. We'll have to talk about this another time, for the rain's stopped and I want to put some finishing touches to my model."

"Oh, don't go! We're just getting started."

"Sorry, but I have to cast it tomorrow." Rather thoughtfully, Dan walked out into the last drops of the cool impersonal rain.

D AN STEPPED back from the completed Minute Man. The Committee had been wise to insist on this larger model which measured just twenty-seven inches in height and looked alive enough to talk.

As Dan shifted his gaze from figure to plow and back again, he experienced the artist's satisfaction in a dream made into reality. No longer need he have those awful sinkings of the heart that he had experienced more than once. This figure was good; it was human, a young man in his own mind's image. Now, if the casting could be done without accident, he would have something to show the town.

To help with the casting, Dan's father had stayed home from the office. Pamela came in to Will's room with him to look at the finished work. "Don't you think you should have a professional do the rest, Dan?"

"I'm a professional!" Dan smiled. "What did I go to New York for?"

"But this is so important."

"I have an able assistant," Dan nodded at his father.

"Well, at least cast it here, dear!" Pamela said. "It was

very thoughtless of me to say you couldn't. I take it all back."

"It's better in the barn," Dan said. "I've got the hogshead it's to stand on set up and the water is drawn."

Patrick, summoned to help them move the model, arrived to stand back and gaze at the figure. For a man who mainly talked potatoes, hay, and calves, he had a fine judgment of less material things. This judgment Dan valued, and the young sculptor eagerly awaited his verdict.

Patrick was in no hurry to give it. "Now there's a young feller for you," he said at last. "Nobody'd climb on *his* back in a horse trade." That was Patrick's highest praise.

"Have you any criticism?" Dan asked.

"That I haven't," Patrick said slowly. "He stands on his own two feet, and he's all related together-like." Patrick walked around the model. "And he's just as good behindt as before. He makes you feel glad thit liberty's comin'—and God save th' British."

After laughing at Patrick's customary poke at his hereditary foes, they got down to the work of moving the model. Dan had constructed the turntable on which it stood, and they wheeled this along the hall into the back entry. Dan and Patrick then lifted the heavy clay model and Dan, being the taller, walked backward feeling with his foot for the first step.

The weight bothered them less than the awkwardness of holding to so small a base. So many points extruded unexpectedly. Patrick's thick farmer-fingers were strong, but they had so short a hold that there was a grave tendency for them to slip. It was difficult, too, trying to bend forward and feel for the step and still not butt one's head into the undried clay.

Once the statue swayed so far that the Judge, who was nursing his way alongside, instinctively put out his hand and pushed in the clay ear.

126

Pamela showed her perturbation by offering advice. Dan sweated, but it was the Judge who mopped his brow. They took a devious but practicable route through the woodshed, along the lane, and across the orchard to the barn, where they set their load down at last. In all that travail Dan had not said a word.

"Sure, and I knew we c'd do it," Patrick said. "He looks like the change of air has done him good already."

Dan was pleased. "It's the change of light." Patrick was right. The figure looked stronger in the stronger light. "Statues ought to be made in the sunlight where they're going to stand," he said as he began repairing the ear. When Pamela departed to clean the house and Patrick went to hoe the cornfield, Dan and his father were left to work out their salvation.

After the cramped space in the house, the barn was delightfully roomy and restful. Stubtail, standing in his stall, occasionally stomped to dislodge a fly, and a door somewhere squeaked in the mild breeze, but the summer day drowsed along while Dan made final changes on his model and his father followed instructions as to handling the plaster of Paris.

Following Dan's instructions, the Judge let the white powder sift through his fingers into a large pan of water until little peaks of it showed above the water. Then Dan gave him an iron spoon with which to stir some blueing into the batch of plaster.

"I promised myself not to ask questions," the Judge said. "But I can't figure the blueing out."

Dan smiled. "How're you going to be a sculptor if you don't ask. The blue plaster is for the first coat. When I chip off the stuff I'll know where I am when I get to the blue. When you finish that job you can start making more white plaster in the other pans."

127

Meanwhile Dan, who had cut pieces of sheet brass into small strips for shims, placed them around the model's head and body. When the plaster had set, this would facilitate a separation from the mold.

By now the blued plaster had reached the right consistency and Dan started to throw it onto the figure, handful by handful. Father and son worked silently, but with great comfort in each other's presence during the slow early stages of the casting. To the Judge, Dan's unhurried processing of the figure was a revelation. Now father was pupil and son instructor. Each stage looked more casual than the last—the taking out of the shims, the laying of iron bars on the outside of the finished mold to give it strength, the fastening of these with burlap soaked in plaster, the laying of the opened mold on the floor and the final scooping out of the clay.

This last operation was nerve-wracking to the older man —it looked so irremediable, this destruction of the sculptor's handiwork built up through the anxious weeks. There would be no second chance. The cast must be perfect or the whole tedious business must be started over again from armature up.

"Can you think of another way?" Dan asked when his father mentioned this.

"No. It's nature way, too. You can't hatch a chicken without breaking the egg. But nature's been at it longer than I have."

Dan liked the way his father had remained sensitive instead of hardening through the years like most men. "Mr. Ward said the sure cure for worry was knowing what you were going to do, and then doing it one step at a time."

"You got your fifty dollars worth of Mr. Ward right there," the Judge said.

The afternoon slumbered on, punctuated only by the distant clock. They scraped the clay out to the last daub, fitted the pieces of the empty mold together, welded them tight with more burlap, and stood the statue on its head. The reason for this, Dan explained, was that the semi-liquid plaster would more surely fill that simple globe where the Minute Man's brains were supposed to be than trickle to his feet.

So far all had gone well. The Judge had grown used to Dan's completing one difficult stage after another without accident. The strain, long and considerable, lessened with each cupful of plaster poured into the filling mold, and the Judge was thankful. He was tired. Trying a difficult case took less out of him than watching his youngest coolly achieve his great objective. But it would soon be over. The mold was already half filled. Dan was steadying it and the Judge was pouring when Dan said, "Stop, father."

His tone was so strained and queer that the Judge knew something was wrong. He followed Dan's gaze. There, spouting from an opening that had burst in the statue's head, ran the white plaster, making an ever-spreading pool on the barn floor.

"Sonny!" the Judge said with bursting heart. To him it looked like the ruin of every hope.

"Hold this, please," Dan said. As soon as his father had taken hold of the mold, Dan picked up a shim and with it and some clay patched up the opening in the head. Already the plaster on the floor was stiffening into mush. Dan quickly made another opening in the statue's back, gathered up handful after handful of the sticky plaster and pushed it inside the mold. "Did you use all the plaster?" he asked his father.

The Judge had. This was the last straw. The older man looked at his son, expecting to see him shaken in despair. "Is it ruined?"

129

"No, I'll get more plaster tomorrow and we'll finish it up —if you can stay."

The Judge marveled. How could a young man with so much at stake keep his emotions in such control! "You mean it hasn't been hurt?"

"I think we caught it in time to set right."

The Judge did not share this optimism. But if Dan could postpone wringing his hands until the morrow, he would too. After placing barrels around the mold to protect it from being knocked over in the dark, they walked across the grass toward the house together.

"Just tell Mother Pamela it's coming along all right," Dan said. "She'd worry."

"You're not going to be in for supper?"

"No," Dan started upstairs. "She knows I promised to take Lucy on a picnic. It's at Egg Rock—the Shakespeare Club."

The Judge heard Dan duck into his room, *whistling*. Then the whistle was smothered while he pulled off his shirt. Youth, he thought, the magnificent. But no, it was more than that. Dan was no thoughtless boy. He knew what was at stake. This was plain self-control and courage.

The river had never been lovelier than on that summer evening, nor had Lucy. Her soft brown hair hung between her shoulders, her hat dangled over her arm, her high-heeled laced boots danced with tassels at the top. But Dan intended to have no mercy on all this feminine fastidiousness. He had had a grueling afternoon and Lucy was going to do her share of the rowing.

It was the river that had revealed to Dan a useful bit of knowledge that young ladies did their best to conceal from their young men. He had discovered that girls had practically unlimited strength for anything—anything, that is, they wanted to do. In every game as children—hide and seek, cops

130

and robbers, skinning the cat, climbing cherry trees, to say nothing of tag—girls had run as fast, battled as valiantly, and evinced as vocal a pugnacity as the boys.

Then they had shot ahead of boys in growth. They became aloof and withdrawn. This was their silly age. They had crushes on one another. They took to dressing up and fiddling with their hair. They repudiated their former playmates as childish. It was as if boys and girls had come to a fork in the road and taken different routes.

Meanwhile, as Dan reflected, the boys were doing some growing on their own account. They formed gangs and likewise did rather foolish things. They had small patience with anyone different from themselves, hunting such creatures down and hazing them. They hung around men's haunts and picked up a second vocabulary, careful to use one way of talking at home and another at recess and school. They found that emulation was the reason for living, in games, in anything requiring endurance and nerve. And finally they found that it was nice to have an audience.

So the sexes came together again, each conscious of its new secrets, each anxious to show off.

"Tired yet?" Dan asked.

"No, of course not."

Dan looked at Lucy. She looked uncommonly pretty bending and pulling, bending and pulling, with the sun glancing up from the water and brightening her already bright eyes. It was doubly relaxing, Dan thought, to lean back against the cushioned stern and see the sex which pretended to be so fragile, pulling him along between the thick-grassed banks of the river moving through the meadows.

Lucy, however, had compensation for her work. The picture of Dan before her won all her satisfied attention. His sprawly length, as always, managed an ease that was never awkward and his eyes were ever interested. It was as if he

131

brimmed with a sunshine not of the day but from some interior source.

Characteristically, he had told Lucy nothing of the afternoon's misadventures. But nowadays the talk always got around to his statue and he was not surprised when Lucy said, "Where would you like to set the Minute Man up, Dan?"

"Providing there is one."

"You know there's going to be one. Things always have gone right for you and they always will."

"Thanks."

"It's true. Haven't you thought about where you'd like it?"

"I've not heard a better suggestion for a site than yours."

"Mine!" Lucy stopped rowing. "When did I ever suggest a site?"

"The same day you said you didn't want a statue of a minute man."

"Oh, Dan! Stop teasing. I've always been crazy about your statue and you know it."

Dan grinned. "You wanted a cannon. And then a pile of muskets."

"Oh, that day!" Lucy laughed.

"And that site," Dan said. He sat up straighter. "I don't want him stuck up there in Buttrick's cow-pasture. And I don't want him at some cross-roads or on the Common where people'll see him so often they won't see him at all. I want them to have to go *look* at him in his natural haunts. Where he did the job."

"I think he'd look wonderful there. I'm going to start persuading people right off."

"Well, in that case, I'll row."

THE CONTINENTAL MINUTE MAN stood on a solid base at the Art Exhibit in the Cattle Show. He had survived his casting. Dan had lettered a sign reading:

CONCORD MINUTE MAN
Model for the statue proposed as per-
manent memorial of The Fight at the
Old North Bridge, April 19, 1775, by
Daniel Chester French

This time his statue stood alone in all its dignity and significance. Dan would have liked to take up his station near enough to hear the people's comments. But his modesty was bone deep.

He was helping Pamela water her exhibit of flowers at the far end of the building, when Louisa May Alcott came up to him, accompanied by her father. He was seventy-four now and the pillar was beginning to lean. But his mind was alert still and his interest in the young intense. Standing there, with cascades of white hair falling down each side of his boulder-like head, he was still impressive. His daughter was now the famous one, thanks to the large and continuing sale of *Little Women*. In fact, her royalties had just taken her on a trip to Europe.

"I hear you've a statue here, Dan," she said. "Come show it to father and me and point out its excellences."

Dan hesitated, having no intention of standing admiringly in front of his own work.

Pamela understood. "You don't go around pointing out the excellences of your book, Louisa," she said a trifle sharply.

Bronson Alcott interrupted this incipient pruning-match by taking Dan's arm and saying, "The true artist evokes a something greater than he and then vanishes in his evocation. So there is no place for self-consciousness. Come on, my boy. Let us study the work together."

Dan could hardly refuse and walked between the old man and his daughter. To his satisfaction they had some difficulty in nearing the statue. Not only Concord men and women, but farmers from Lincoln and Acton and Carlisle were intently gathered before this prototype of their own forefathers. Dan heard one burly bearded man say to another, "Means business, that boy, eh?"

"Danged if he don't, Sam," said the other. "He's a hard-hitter, that chap is. Got good shoulders on him."

This pleased Dan, whose chief anxiety had been that the ordinary man of the fields might find his young farmer pretty.

"Look at his buttons! Ain't they natural!" cried a young girl. "And that hand on his plow!"

" 'And God help the British' says I, when ever I sees it," came a voice from the other side. Patrick was showing someone the statue with the same look of pride a father bears when he shows off his new-born son. Dan was simultaneously amused and touched.

Recognizing Mr. Alcott, the men beside the statue made way for him. The others melted back a little and the old man came face to face with the creation.

"There, Father!" Louisa said.

Dan waited for the veteran critic's verdict. Under the bushy eyebrows keen eyes were giving the figure no desultory glance. Dan noticed the thick lips working and Bronson Alcott said, "It stirreth my blood. . . . Louisa, it stirreth the blood in my old veins . . . youth's magnanimity." Then he lifted his head and voice and proclaimed to the circle, as well as to Dan, "There will be but one opinion and that entirely favorable." He put a heavy hand on Dan's shoulder. "It was inspiration that enabled you to depict this modest valor, Dan. I am glad I have lived to see this."

Dan flushed, embarrassed but reinforced by so moving a benediction. He scarcely heard Louisa's comment, "He *is* a tidy bird!" an expression she had no doubt picked up in London. He was glad to divert the talk to her travels as they left the ever-renewed circle of onlookers, asking her what was the most memorable event of her trip.

"Oh, a talk with Henry James, by all means!" Louisa said. "He is so funny in his English plumage pecking up every grain of Concord news I could give him."

Presently Dan excused himself and walked back to his stepmother. Perhaps he might make a businesslike person yet. Certainly it had been a happy stroke of genius when he had suggested exhibiting his statue here at the Cattle Show before the vote at Town Meeting. The crowd seemed with him. It was easy, of course, to "Oh!" and "Ah!" over his Continental, and quite another to be taxed to pay for it. But he was heartened.

Two days later Dan was presented with a premium of $15 for his model, which was nothing less than magnificent at Concord's fair.

Town Meeting had been called for the first Tuesday in November. It had seeped into the mind of the least important Concordian that the Centennial of the Concord Fight must be properly observed, and that the celebration was now only a year and a half away.

At first Pamela had made jokes, as was her wont when Concord vaunted her self-importance. And when it was decided to invite the President of the United States, she burst into laughter.

"Oh, unworldly Concord!" she cried, lifting her eyes in mock devotion. "And why not Queen Victoria also, in mourning for her lost Bridge? Blessed are the meek, and we shall have the United States Marine Band here to score that point."

But the possibility of Dan's participation muted Pamela's wittiest asides. "Of course if they wish to invite the world here to see Dan unveil his statue, I have nothing to say," she remarked.

"Probably that's just as well," the Judge smiled. "But I hear you're to have something to say, Dan."

"What do you mean by that?" Pamela demanded.

"He has to turn advocate for his work at Town Meeting."

"Why can't the Minute Man speak for him?" She turned to Dan. "What sort of speech do you have to make?"

"Explanatory—matter-of-fact. Nothing to worry about. I'll be there to answer questions, chiefly."

Dan had not lost any sleep over this public appearance. He would know nearly everyone in the hall, and he had been living for this day so many months that he was long since primed for the encounter.

Yet on that morning dark with the threat of sleet he woke feeling a little queasy. Would it be as simple as he thought, asking a roomful of men to spend a lot of money for a statue when the panic had made everyone feel so pinched?

136

This thought oppressed Dan more and more as he walked to the meeting where he and Patrick had stood the model in front of the assembly, to the right of the moderator's desk. By the time George Keyes had called the meeting to order, the room was filled and some people were standing. On account of an important hearing in Boston, Judge French was unable to be there and Pamela preferred to wait at home. But Sallie sat by her husband in the rear, and the room was peppered with staid men whom Dan knew would give his project just consideration.

The meeting was called to order and a tedious hour was consumed on routine business. Then the moderator cleared his throat and said, "Now we come to a question of great moment in connection with the Centennial. It has been suggested that we epitomize the crucial day of our young country's past in some permanent manner. After much consideration our committee has decided that a statue is the best means of evoking the solemn memories of that day. It so happens that our friend and neighbor, Mr. Dan French, had an idea of the same sort and at the same time. He has made a statue of the Minute Man to symbolize April 19, 1775. You have already seen it at the Cattle Show and it stands before you here. The question before us is whether we think this statue suitable for our purpose, or shall we instruct our Committee to look farther. First, I shall call on the Chairman of the Committee to enlighten us on certain points: Mr. John Keyes."

The blood was beginning to throb in Dan's temples; he was to speak next. The gloom of the day and the defeat of most of the motions put before the meeting, because of the panic and money situation, had made him nervous. He could barely pin his attention on Mr. Keyes. Far off he heard a voice recounting the stages of the Committee's investigation.

137

They had considered a memorial bridge but found it too expensive for these times; then a spirited painting; a new wing to the school; a perpetual scholarship at Harvard; an illuminated history of the Fight; or some monument other than the statue.

"All these projects had merit," Mr. Keyes continued. "But we were tossed between considerations of cost, appropriateness, and lasting qualities. Then one evening, while we were in discussion in Mr. Emerson's study, the answer to our problem literally came to us. Mr. Dan French *brought* it in his hands. This answer seemed so complete that but one action was left to us—to refer it to your judgment. I now call upon the sculptor of the Minute Man to lay before you the facts of his offer."

The applause was moderate as Dan walked to his model and stood beside it. He looked younger than his twenty-three years. Somewhere between his chair and the statue he had left any self-consciousness behind. As he stood looking at these people who were to decide his statue's destiny, and perhaps his own, Sallie thought that her brother's beautifully shaped head, animated features, and handsome eyes were a sufficient persuasion in themselves. He certainly did not look scared. And his voice was composed, conversational, as if he had all the confidence in the world. With a sigh of relief she settled back to listen.

"I'm glad Mr. Keyes suggests I stick to the facts," Dan said. "They are few in number. The idea is to celebrate what happened. Well, the chief thing that happened was rebellion against an unjust act. If Concord is to remember anyone, I think it should be the man who left his plow and caught up his flintlock so that we could be free masters of our lives.

"I didn't have to grope for a subject, although nobody in Concord has fathered as many children as I did minute men.

138

I must have had a family of thirty, in every possible pose. And then this fellow came about."

Dan paused to let them gaze. The room was very quiet.

"My proposition is this: I agree to make a seven foot model of this statue and deliver a plaster cast to the town, if this meeting will pay the expenses incurred, not to exceed $350. I agree to have this work completed in good time so that the finished statue, of granite or bronze, may be set up well before the anniversary. I trust you will vote for bronze. The granite statue can be cut for $1000 while it will cost $500 more to cast it in bronze. But the bronze will endure for your children's children to see; to keep the granite intact we shall have to change our climate."

Only one or two smiled at this suggestion. Mention of costs in this panic year had been a damper.

"One thing more," Dan continued. "It is hardly fitting for the sculptor to push his work onto the community. It must speak for itself. Let us suppose that the town feels it extravagant to erect such a memorial now. Fifty years from now, when the next anniversary arrives, it may be too late. Already I find it difficult to obtain an authentic plow of 1775. The flintlock has all but disappeared. Father and I had to drive to Acton to find the powder horn. The clothes worn on that day will moulder away. But most important of all, the American nation in 1925 may be too grand, too occupied with its affairs, to care about our simple exertions at the old North Bridge. Already the terrible battles of the War just past make our little Fight so small as to be hardly worth considering, unless the object of it is remembered. A handful of farmers opposed the greatest military power of the time that they might continue to be free. That fact must never be forgotten. That is the fact which it is Concord's privilege to ask our country to remember."

Applause broke in from all sides. Dan thanked the room

139

for its attention, offered to answer any questions, and went back to his seat. He did not feel elated. He had meant to say something complimentary to Concord, to mention at least how much he had owed to Concord. He felt a hand on his shoulder. Fanny Hubbard was leaning forward. "I didn't know you were an orator," she whispered.

The moderator asked if there were any remarks.

A farmer stood up and was recognized. "All this sounds very nice," he said, "but do you know what I'm getting for my milk today? Less than it costs me. It don't pay me to cut my hay, for my cows would be less of a loss to me if they died of starvation. I can't give my eggs away and the fatter a hog gits, the more he costs me. I don't say there should be no celebration. I do say cut out the trimmings. The celebration the gentlemen have planned is going to cost $5000 if it costs a cent. That means the tax rate'll be pushed up again, and what will the likes of me do when we can't pay now? I don't doubt the statue'd be nice enough, but living comes first, and I vote against it."

"Same here," said the next man recognized. "There's one monument at the Bridge now, and who goes to look at it? Nobody. I hear this one might be raised on Buttrick's hill. And how many'd drive out there? Certainly we don't want our Common cluttered up with statuary. I hold with John Perkins, this is no time to incur extra expense. I also hold that we don't want any more statues, good, bad, or indifferent."

"Don't fergit—Ebby Hubbard's already give a thousand dollars fer a statue," a third speaker reminded them.

And so it went while Dan listened. He had never realized before how heavily poverty lay on his neighbors. The statue cost money. That was its crime. That was why it was on trial. When Judge Hoar rose to express the opinion that Dan's offer of $350 was too little to cover his expenses, suggesting that the motion, when made, should substitute $500, a new furore of objection was raised.

Fear seeped into Dan's consciousness. Those who spoke in his statue's favor mentioned its grace or its appropriateness or the fact that Dan was not asking remuneration for his work. They did little to answer those, like farmer Perkins, who had literally no money, and no wish to go into debt for a "falderol," as one impoverished shopkeeper called it.

The day wore on and the crucial moment of voting neared. Dan was tired, unhappy, and fearful.

"Are you ready for the question?" the moderator asked.

Mr. Emerson rose and was recognized. He seemed thinner than ever, but his voice had not lost its vigor, its matchless power to charm. Surrounding the man was an indefinable atmosphere of benediction. Even before his first words, the room was invested with a new and greater presence and the listeners ceased to stir.

"Friends, is this the town I know?" came the voice. "Is this the Concord of whom we are so proud? On that great day which we plan to celebrate, the men of Concord considered ends, knowing that if the ends were just and good, the means would be found.

"Today we seek a worthy way to honor those men and women whom we cannot repay. Providence, in its unforeseen way, has offered us the means. This statue of a nameless Minute Man tells the story. While Concord lives it will tell that story to all who come after us, the story that our forefathers made plain to history. It will remind Americans of the virtues without which no country can endure—the resolve, the self-reliance, the unshakeable knowledge that the value of freedom is not argueable.

"These are hard times; let us not make them ignoble as well. Let us not witness the humiliation of seeing a dozen

141

towns bidding for the privilege of erecting this statue which the artist offers to us. Concord could never live down this pettiness. Let us distinguish our town and the occasion, for ages to come, by accepting the young man's offer without further parley. Mr. Moderator, I think we are ready for the question."

The stately voice ceased, the great man sat down. A choke came into Dan's throat, a sense of gratitude and of liberation.

"All in favor of the motion please say aye."

From all around him the ayes came in volume.

"Opposed, no."

The scattering of Noes was feeble. Dan drew a long breath of relief.

"The Ayes have it," the moderator said. "And may I add my personal comment. The Town of Concord has lived up to its reputation for sober common sense this day."

Pamela was getting supper. She flew into the front hall as she heard the door open. Her black eyes were shining question marks as Dan and his father entered from the station. Dan's face was the answer.

"Dan! You won! They've accepted the statue!"

"This is a great day for the French family," said the Judge as he kissed his wife.

"Did they have much of a fight over the commission?" Pamela asked.

"That question never came up," Dan said, a little tightly for he knew what his practical stepmother was going to say.

"You mean they aren't going to pay you anything?" Pamela's eyes flashed in coming storm.

"The resolution calls for expenses—costs, rent of studio, if I have one, and the casting, but I contribute my services."

"But how ridiculous! If they employ a carpenter to repair the Town Hall, they have to pay him. Then why not you?"

"It's a little different," the Judge came to Dan's rescue. "The town is venturing a good deal in engaging a young man who has never done a statue to make this important work."

"Oh, fiddlesticks!" Pamela cried. "They simply want something for nothing in the usual Yankee fashion. So they seize Dan's youth as an excuse."

"Look at it this way, Mother Pamela," Dan said. "It's a terrific opportunity. If I do this job it'll stand there as long as I live, and my reputation will be made."

"Reputation for letting people walk over you!" Pamela retorted.

"I don't agree with you," the Judge intervened. "From what Dan has told me, a request for payment would have been the last straw."

"It was only Mr. Emerson saved the Minute Man as it was," Dan added.

"How absolutely grotesque!" Pamela cried. "The sculptor is to get no money because he may get some reputation! Only a town of philosophers could conceive of such a thing. You are to be paid nothing because the work is so good! Fancy!" Suddenly she sniffed the air. "There! My blueberry muffins are burning!"

Dan and his father were left alone.

"Don't mind mother's outburst," the Judge said. "A woman's loyalty is a wonderful thing to have."

"I'll need it," Dan said. "Now that I've got the job I'm a bit scared. Anyway," and his confident smile came back, "my winter's work is decided."

CHAPTER

17

NEXT MORNING Dan woke from an uneasy sleep. He had an unaccustomed sense of burden. Then, as his consciousness cleared it came back with a bang. Town Meeting! And *he* was the one pledged to make a statue seven feet high!

His sinking of the stomach was soon supplanted by a rising of spirits. The dire and glorious responsibility was on him. He had been charged by his town to make the Minute Man, but where?

By the time he had reached the breakfast table Dan was again his composed, none-too-serious self. "Where do you suppose people make seven foot statues?" he asked.

"Not in Will's room, thank goodness!" Pamela exclaimed.

"Patrick would rather like you to do it in the barn," the Judge said. "He says he's willing to go down in bronze as the defier of the British. You could get a worse model, Dan."

"I can't see Patrick posing in the nude at zero."

"Mercy! You aren't going to have the Minute Man nude!" Pamela gasped.

"Mother Pamela, have you lived this long as a sculptor's

144

overseer without discovering that you can't put clothes on a body until you've got the body?"

Pamela was downright surprised. "It's the effect of clothes you want, wrinkles and all, so why go around Robin Hood's barn to do a body first?"

"Because sculpture isn't skin-deep, any more than beauty is. First the skeleton, then the muscles and skin, *then* the garments. The only place we skimp on is the underwear. No red flannels for my Continental, and he won't change his shirt twice a week."

They canvassed the studio possibilities of Concord and could think of nothing. Neither May Alcott nor Dr. Rimmer knew of one. And when the Boston real estate people were approached it was as if Dan had asked for the nearest den of lions. A studio? What for? Oh, sculpture. No. You won't find anything like that, not in Boston.

"All I want is a room with a ceiling ten feet high and a north light, if there's no skylight, and it should have running water," Dan said over and over, but it was an exasperating frustration. The best anyone could suggest was an office building on Tremont Street at Bromfield ambitiously misnamed the Studio Building. The one vacancy in that edifice was a long narrow room with only one window.

After two days of search, the most tiring, maddening days he had known, he resignedly came back to the Studio Building. Inside, a young man in a clay-daubed smock was talking to the janitor. The smock encouraged Dan to introduce himself. "It looks as if we were in the same trade," he said to the young man who turned out to be Martin Milmore, another hopeful sculptor.

Milmore's reply to Dan's question about vacancies was more friendly than encouraging. He had scouted the city himself and found nothing. "Boston is shy of sculptors to a degree I could never have believed," Milmore said. "The city employs every means of thwarting and averting sculptors. The Hub of the Universe, and no studios! And when you get one, no heat! If you take that room upstairs, I warn you, French, you'll have to keep a bucket of snow to keep your ears from being frost-bitten. The only way I warm up is by talking to the janitor."

Dan was amused. After Milmore had cited the example of two other artists, Porter and Munzig, who had also been fooled into renting rooms in the building, he and Milmore went up again to look at Room 35.

"With a turntable you could do it," Milmore said. "At any rate there's one advantage in working in a cavern like this—you'll know how your statue will look at night."

Dan laughed and Milmore laughed with him. This nonsense decided Dan. Better to struggle in the dark with congenial company than waste more time wandering over the city.

A large turntable was made to Dan's order and the tools of his profession arrived—iron, pipe, wood and wire. Patrick hitched Stubtail to the sledge, for an early snowstorm made carriage travel difficult, and drove Dan in with the twenty-seven inch model of the Minute Man.

With the heavy plaster, the two men struggled upstairs to Room Thirty-five. Patrick was amazed at the miscellaneous litter. "If you'd told me you were a hardware dealer changin' over to the plumbin' business after failin' as a carpenter, I'd believe you," he said.

"Everybody ought to start life as a carpenter," Dan said. "Sculptor or hangman, you've got to know how to use tools. There's so much to do first that I haven't ordered the clay yet."

"How much of that?" Patrick asked.

"I'll start off with 700 pounds."

146

"When you get all this iron foundry in him, I won't be carryin' him down."

"We'll take him apart for the mold," Dan explained. "And he'll be cast by professionals in a regular shop—that is if they authorize bronze."

"They'd better after you doin' all this work," Patrick said with a glint in his fine eyes. "I'm glad it's you and not me that's doin' it."

"It's fun," Dan said. "I'll tell you a secret if you promise to keep it to yourself. An artist is just a person who carries enjoyment to extremes."

Patrick pushed back his cap and scratched his forehead. "I thought they called them drunks."

Dan laughed aloud. "You probably can tell the difference, Patrick. The drunk would give anything to be able to stop drinking. I've talked to them at the Middlesex Hotel and I know. The artist, on the other hand, gives everything to be allowed to work. It's his big happiness, as I'm finding out."

"I told you it'd come to you if you let it, didn't I?" Patrick asked.

"Yes you did, and you were right," Dan said. "I'll never forget that morning you and I had that talk in the asparagus patch. You have a very easy way of lecturing a fellow, Patrick."

"Oh, that's nothin'. That's the way I lecture meself."

It was fortunate that Dan could so easily reconcile himself to the prosaic preliminaries of statue-making. He wrote his brother,

You ought to see me grubbing around with this skeleton. But I've always said that all play and no work makes Jack a dull boy. I must say I like thinking with tools. Sallie can't understand how anyone has the patience to go through all this tedium of preparation. Yet she is willing to sew and cut and try on a dress some thousands of times before going to dance. It's all in what you like. Her Ned accepts a long walk through briers and alders for a little good fishing and never complains, not even of the walk back, when he has caught nothing. It's the absorption that counts. Sometimes I think it isn't very complimentary to oneself to enjoy most the thing that makes one forget oneself. But that's art. We can discuss. We're all looking forward to your Christmas visit. Let me know day and train of your arrival and I'll meet you at the station in Boston and bring you to see these operations in Room 35, Studio Building, a sort of frozen Black Hole of Calcutta.

Through that November Dan worked steadily and hard. He broke off in December to model his cousin Frank's baby in New York. The $300 offered by Frank and Ellen was not only Dan's top price so far but a reassuring indication that his reputation was growing. Also the money was a substantial help in the lean months ahead.

Will's arrival solidified the Christmas joy for Dan, whose feeling for his elder brother was compounded of real affection and a worshipful attitude dating back to childhood. Dan would have been the last to see that he was slowly approaching his brother in achievement and local repute. And Will would have been the last to begrudge the change of status. The reunion was full of mutual admiration and Dan was thankful that he could unlock the door of his studio with confidence and pride.

Will French was deeply moved by his brother's work. "It's strong, Dan. Stronger than those photographs indicated."

"This is the later model," Dan said.

148

"What with letters from Sallie and father and you, I've lost count. Just how many models have you made?"

"First, some charcoal sketches years ago, after a trip to the Bridge with Lucy. It was disagreeing with her that first put the idea in my head."

Will smiled. "Women are very useful, even disputing with them helps."

"Second, some little clay sketches after I returned from studying with Ward in New York—around the time Cousin John Keyes said it was a pity I wasn't older and more experienced. It's one of those sketches that I took to Mr. Emerson who started the ball rolling. After there was a twenty-seven inch model that father and I nearly broke in casting. I saw some little improvements I could make and so I did this model and had Gary cast it. This is the one that did the trick at the Town Meeting. The seven-footer will be the fifth."

Tearing his gaze away from the model Will looked at Dan. "And there was one time that we began to think you'd never find anything you wanted to do!"

"It was mighty gradual I admit," Dan smiled. "Even now I couldn't pick out any one moment when I decided to become a sculptor. I still think Patrick's right. You grow into what you're going to do if you grow honestly, and the desire grows with you. I've ten times the desire now that I had when I did the bust of your head. It's that desire that takes you a bit farther than you expected."

"But there must have been a place where you made a big jump. This model's an enormous advance on what you did before."

"I had an enormously bigger incentive. I *had* to take advantage of this big opportunity."

"And the power came?" Will asked.

"Yes, but don't make it mysterious. Something tells you

149

you aren't satisfied with something. In my case it was the plow. I made that plow over till I nearly went crazy."

"But you didn't quit. That's the point."

"You don't quit because you want it better. You think you've got his arm right. Next day you wonder. The day after that you bring yourself to try another position, and *that's* better. It's a good eye that knows when to stop."

"By the way, I stopped off in New York to see Frank and Ellen, and they're tickled pink over that bust of the baby."

Dan sobered. "Two or three like that and I'd be in an asylum. I did the child with a low necked dress slipping off one shoulder to show the little curves. Then Ellen said, 'No, the sweet thing had always worn a high-necked dress' so I spent two or three days changing the sweet thing's clothes and making it less attractive. And then we had a struggle over the tongue. Do you think it looks idiotic with its tongue like it is?"

"Not quite," Will smiled.

"That's the beauty of working to order," Dan said wrathfully. "You've got to follow the prescription. If Ellen had wanted the baby smoking a pipe, I would have had to oblige. Ellen didn't like the way I'd done the child's mouth. She said it would never look like her 'dear little angel' unless it showed its 'dear little tongue.' So its dear little tongue is shown. I'll say this—no other baby in the world was ever modeled with its tongue out, and I never made $300 so swiftly."

"Is it a great temptation to stop and model babies until you've made your first hundred thousand?"

Dan shook his head. "I just told you it was the desire that drove you to do something better than you expected. Well, if you kill the desire, what have you?"

"Good," Will said quietly with deep satisfaction.

They took the train from North Station to Concord.

"Which girl has first call on your time now?" Will asked. "Lucy?"

Dan pretended to look perplexed. "William, there's safety in numbers. I now know many pretty girls, any one of whom might make a man happy, if it were not for the others. That's why I'm still free."

"It's probably just as well."

"I don't know about that." Dan tapped his brother on the knee. "Remember, we've got to talk seriously about this —ten years from today."

The train passed Walden and the still unfrozen Pond reminded Dan of a Concord picnic the summer before.

"I drove the crowd home in the Dearborn supplied with extra seats. All the youth and beauty of Concord was in that wagon and I ran it into a tree. I thought horses were supposed to see. The mosquitoes were thick as you please. So was the sarcasm. No eight humans have ever laughed so much in any one evening. Do you know, Will, I hate to grow up."

"Is there any danger?" Will glanced at his handsome happy brother. "Some people stay young forever."

"I'll be twenty-four next April."

"What of it? Years aren't the measure. It's what you do. How many fellows your age are entrusted by a town with an important commission? Father must be busting with pride."

"Well, he's managed not to bust yet. He spends his days waiting for your arrival—William the Conqueror. Which reminds me, Will, I've got 'em all lined up for you. We've planned theatricals and tableaux with grand scenic effects, dissolving statues, panoramas, blue fire, lovely girls, Grecian costumes, tremendous applause, crowded houses. Lucy and I have written a beautiful little play called 'The Tempter

Hath a Snare For All' based on father's favorite remark—"
"Concord. . . . CON-*CORD!*" sang out the brakeman.

Looking out the window, Will caught sight of his father in the sleigh behind Stubtail. He got out of his seat and followed tall Dan down the aisle. Life was pretty good when it could provide homecomings like this.

CHAPTER

18

JANUARY SAW the tall skeleton draped in inexpressive clay, and the question of a model had soon to be answered. Boston was still the literary lantern in the nation's window but almost devoid of artists and therefore of models.

Dan's workshop resembled an anatomy student's laboratory. In addition to a skeleton and a copy of Houdon's *Skinned Man,* Dan had been allowed to borrow with the help of Mr. Emerson a plaster cast of the Apollo Belvedere from The Athenaeum.

Ironically Dan had trained his eye and hand to copy these rigid models to such perfection that their rigidity was transferred to the clay. He needed to observe the fluid movement of the living flesh.

By now Dan had decided that the students of sculpture whom he had run into, while genial and good fun, were not much to count on. The talk of these fellows was largely of the body for the body, and their conduct followed their talk. Dan's up-bringing had been different. His instincts, as strong as anybody's, had been disciplined into a wholesome restraint, and the reward was obvious to all. The conviction had slowly grown up in him that a way of living that is nourished by the insignificant can hardly bear important fruit. So he continued to give drink, passion, and profanity a wide berth and kept to ways that were out in the sun.

Dan had been tempted to ask Milmore to pose for the Minute Man, yet his body lacked the attractive health the farmer-soldier should have. One day in desperation, Dan stripped to the waist, stood in front of the mirror he had bought for his work, and began to copy his own lines and curves.

This was all very well for the chest view, but required squirming to get the shoulders, and the back was anatomically impossible. That night Dan called on Judd Colgan who had shown some interest in his work.

Just twenty-one—the age of the Minute Man—Judd had an open, frank, and fearless face, and his body had been tempered in the fires of summer activity and hardened in the frost.

"What chores are now occupying your time?" Dan asked when they had sat down in the farm kitchen.

"Readying to cut ice, Dan."

"I need a living model for my statue, Judd. I can't pay you much, but enough to hire a man in your place for the cutting and a little over. Could you spare me a few days?"

"Sure. What do I have to do?"

"Just keep a pose for a little while. There are rests in between."

"I guess I can do that all right."

"You won't mind standing around with nothing much on?"

"Why should I? It's the same as going swimming, ain't it?"

"Better. No flies. Can you start tomorrow?"

"Sure thing."

His Minute Man, thought Dan, must have been straight-forward like Judd, and when you came down to it, what finer type American was there?

Judd's assistance marked the beginning of Dan's first feeling of satisfaction in this stage of his work. The clay that had hung dead and heavy on its framework now began to take living shape. With Judd to model, Dan's hands were freer to transfer the observations of his eye. He was even encouraged to think it might be as easy to make the large figure as the smaller, despite the greater amount of manual labor. This labor, Dan thought, was compensated for by the steadiness and stability of the larger work.

"Someday I'm going to come to the hard place," Dan said.

"No use asking for it," Judd observed. "You take on as if you'd been making seven-footers all your life."

With the passing of February Judd could no longer be spared from the farm. By now Dan was by way of becoming a celebrity. People like Charlie Baird came to him and said, "I want to be in on this, Dan. What'll I say when my grandchildren ask, 'What part of the Minute Man is you, Grandpa?'"

Dan laughed and promised he should be at least a leg. And as time wore on Jim Melvin and Charlie Almy, Albert Brown and John Nichols, Arthur King and Roberts and Ragnor, all made their contributions as models for the sake of posterity. One less happy result of Dan's ever-widening notoriety was the number of curious Concordians who came to see him at his studio.

Some visitors were helpful. Dr. Rimmer found much to praise. May Alcott, on the other hand, shook Dan's assurance considerably with her adverse views. Then May's father and Mr. Emerson called, and their quiet commendation helped to re-establish his confidence.

The work itself wasn't the only trouble. Dan was worrying over rumors of Concord's economizing on his project. It was known that the town would be asked to contribute $5000 for the elaborate Centennial celebration with its decorations, entertainment for distinguished visitors, and reception for the President of the United States, his staff, and the military. Therefore $1500 was as much money as Dan dared ask for the statue, although he had discovered that it would cost $2300 to cast it in bronze, not counting the cost of the material. He was in heavy spirits when Concord's most awesome citizen presented himself in his doorway. It was Judge Hoar, who had just come up from Washington to attend the spring Town Meeting.

"You haven't much of a place here," was the Judge's disconcerting remark.

Feeling that a very heavy black dog was perched on his back, Dan watched while the white-bearded man with the sharp eyes inspected the half-finished work. Dan hoped that the clay would not melt under the intentness of the fiery gaze. The Judge shifted his stand, held his wrist behind his back, and said nothing. And Dan, tired, upset, waited in a dull agony of suspense.

"Interesting!" said the Judge at last. "You may have the last word yet."

"How so?" Dan had no idea what Judge Hoar was talking about.

"This figure will speak of Concord's vanished greatness when the town is a mere suburb of Boston and the past is washed from the minds of the surrounding people."

"Then you think it promises?" Dan ventured.

"It is," said the older man. "It doesn't need to promise." He looked at Dan. "When we commissioned this, Dan, I felt that we were expecting too much. But it pays—for certain people."

"I'm the one who's expecting too much now," Dan was

156

emboldened to say. "Sir, I want my statue cast in bronze."

"It must be bronze, of course."

"They'll not vote it so," Dan said. "This is the worst year to expect it. I've scarcely done any work all day for thinking about it. But I had a wild idea, and maybe you are the one who can bring it about. You've read about those condemned cannon the Government intends to dispose of?"

"I know. Hundreds of brass cannon, good for nothing."

"But statues." Dan was taking hope from the Judge's face. "If you induced the Government to contribute a dozen of those cannon—"

"Why not?" Judge Hoar interrupted. "They're our cannon. That's what people forget. The Government's only ourselves." He had opened a little black memorandum book. "I'll petition for twenty of them this session. The party owes me a thing or two." He glanced at Dan with new respect. "You've got a head on your shoulders."

"Well, you've taken a big load off them," Dan said.

Judge Hoar took a final look at the Minute Man, nodded, and left. Dan sprawled out on a chair. Now he was too happy to work. The Minute Man would be cast in bronze.

Extremes breed extremes, and the more profound was Dan's concentration in the studio, the more hilarious were his carryings-on outside.

At the Town Hall he staged "The Dream of Fair Women." He was best man or usher at half-a-dozen weddings. When the birds arrived, he lived as much as possible on the river. He danced. He saw a good deal of Beth Hoar, who was more a princess than ever and whose temperament was poles apart from his. But he preferred sparring with her to listening to compliments from others.

One evening Beth was wearing a handsome gown of yellow and white silk which made her look more stunning than

157

ever. Knowing this made her determined to get the best of Dan, who could usually talk circles about her. She had been watching Dan having his usual good time with various partners, but when he came to ask her for a dance, she took it into her head to refuse. This suited Dan, who was also in a mood for a fray.

"What does a girl get out of being obstinate?" he asked. "A sense of superiority?"

"You know I don't need to cultivate a sense of superiority," Beth said. "You've often told me I already have one."

"Then why not dance?"

"Because it simply is not good for a young man to have his own way so much."

"*I?*" Dan concealed his smile. "As if I didn't spend my life thinking of others."

"That's just it. Too many others. And too confidently. Someday someone will upset your conceit by saying no."

"Do you suppose that doesn't happen?" Dan asked. "Only last evening I called on Nellie Barnes to ask her to go boating, but Henry Wheeler pleaded his case so pathetically that I had to give way for him."

"You see?" Beth said. "You twist everything into a virtue. That's the acme of conceit."

"Now you interest me," Dan said. "All my life I've heard of people being conceited, when I thought they were just having a good time. What is it? Last summer a girl you know raked me over the coals for being conceited. Took me completely by surprise."

"But I like it!" Beth said. "When a man is conceited I like to have him show it, as you do."

"How do I show it?" Dan asked.

"Only a conceited man would ask that," Beth said. "Let's change the subject."

"You're not going to slide out of it that way," Dan said.

158

"I see I drew blood," Beth looked into his face and laughed.

"Not that way," Dan tried not to laugh. "If I said that I liked cross-eyed girls, like you, or girls who had part gypsy blood, like you, you'd not change the subject. Or would you?" Dan enjoyed the look of astonished insult on Beth's features.

"I must say you think of grotesque things."

"No more grotesque than your calling me conceited and then trying to back out of it. Do I go around *boasting*?"

"No."

"Do I infer that your company, for example, is not good enough for me?"

"No."

"Then how am I conceited?"

"In wanting to be always right," Beth said.

"Oh, no, that's the man of me," Dan said. "And your wanting to be always right is the woman of you."

"But I don't!" Beth protested.

"Good. Then we'll dance." Dan stood up and held out his hands. "Please?" He laughed. "Conceited people never say please."

Beth rose too.

Life was very gay, very engrossing, and very delightful.

But it was full of endless endeavor as well. For some time Dan had pondered May Alcott's criticisms. She had considered the shoulders too high and felt that the rear leg dragged. Perhaps. Yet he could not bear to make his young man less tall, less buoyant. Depressing his shoulders might make him slightly more matter-of-fact, but squat. He would not do it.

The leg, however, could be improved. If Dan had learned anything in sculpture, it was how great a difference a small

159

change could make. To effect this change one had first to see the perfect line in the mind's eye, in spite of what the clay was saying.

For a week Dan tried to fix this line in his mind while he worked on the Minute Man's hair and hat. Should the hair be blown? Smooth? Short? Long? Medium? How much should be covered by the hat? How jaunty the hat? How much roll to the brim? Questions, problems everywhere. Art was a succession of choices. The Minute Man was not in reality clay but the sum of a thousand decisions. "Just as I am," Dan said to himself in a reflective moment.

One morning Dan looked at his calendar and started! April 18, 1874. In one year and a day his statue must be in position.

Suddenly a year seemed a short measure of time. He must end this hideous indecision; the legs must be finished this day.

He stood in front of his soldier. If he moved the right leg forward an inch, it would speed up the tempo, make his man brisker. A tedious operation. But he could keep the line he had, which was admirable, by sticking pegs on the front, putting clay on them, and then taking an equal amount off the back.

That day Dan had no visitors, opened the door to no knocks, let lovely voices sift by unheard. It was his longest day, but when the twilight made him stop he had finished, and the work was justified.

The sleeve came next. For this, Patrick left his own spring plowing and came in to assist the Minute Man's maker. He, like the Continental, had just quit plowing and the blood still flowed swiftly through his veins. They must stand out a little, Dan thought, as Patrick's did.

"Sure, and he's coming along now!" Patrick exclaimed as

he saw the almost finished statue. "It's nice he's to stand outdoors. He belongs outdoors, that man."

"You feel that?" Dan asked happily.

"He's sure of himself, too. I like that," Patrick said. "He knows there's no deceit in him, and so he's not afraid."

Dan was touched by the trueness of this rough man's observation. "If it had been right to make him resemble anyone, Patrick, I'd've had him resemble you."

Patrick's blue eyes left the statue. It was the first time Dan had ever seen him surprised. "Now that was a narrow escape —fer the statue."

"Remember that time you let me plow?" Dan asked. "I got the taste of ambition then. And do you remember the time you told me to be faithful to myself?"

"Sure and I never had the tongue to say that."

"Yes you did, you told me to grow along and let my work grow out of me naturally."

"Well a man can't be too careful what he says!" Patrick admitted with a smile. "But it's the truth."

"So you see you had a hand in this statue."

"Well, I'll throw it up to me wife when she gits after me," Patrick said, covering his pleasure with modesty and a joke.

The plow necessitated more armature and endless measurements. Dan had discovered a model out in the Cattle Show grounds. The sun was hot on his back as he copied it, a reminder that time was racing along, held back by no plow. But when he added it to his statue, he could see the satisfaction in the faces of his committee. It gave stability to the figure.

Next Dan concentrated on the right hand that was to hold the musket. Milmore helped him make a cast of his own hand. "It's not every sculptor who can have a finger so literally in his own pie," Milmore said.

161

The musket was tedious. After a long search Dan had found the flintlock he desired at a woodcarver's shop. But time was crowding him. He worked on Decoration Day. He absented himself from the Fourth of July ceremonies to work on the symbol of its cause.

The coat was almost a despair. It had to be thrown carelessly over the brace, and this required much thought to make it look hasty yet not disjointed.

At last came a day when the front of the statue seemed completed. Then the back was finished. Yet always some final touch was needed, especially on the head.

The varieties of emotion expressible in the pose of a head was a surprising revelation to Dan. Nobody had told him that the triumphant effect of his statue was to depend on the precise line of his man's chin. The figure had to imply the glorious outcome of that day—which was the United States of America—without transcending the credible bounds of a farm boy's mode of carrying himself. This was the first moment of freedom's dawning. Yet the figure must not be a braggart, nor cocky, yet not too modest either.

Dan now sweated in the studio where he had been so cold. He hardly knew the moment when it came over him that his statue was done, for it went on living in his mind. It had always been living in his mind, it seemed to him now. It was as much part of him as his spine. The idea had sunk into the very roots of him and he could no more say goodbye to it than to the eyes that had given it birth. But the professional casters were ready.

The Committee was so pleased with the finished statue that they declared it must be shown before being taken for casting to the Ames Foundry in Chicopee. Dan was requested to hold a reception at the studio.

About an hour before the time fixed for the party, Dan

heard a knock on his door and admitted a young woman leading an elderly soul who was blind. He was at once struck by the benign face of the blind woman.

"Mother has heard of you and your work, Mr. French," said the daughter. "Although she cannot see, she has trained herself to gain much from descriptions. We hoped it would not be too great an imposition to ask you to describe your statue, as only you can."

"I'm a great nuisance," the blind woman said with energy. "I pray that you may never have to borrow eyes to see this world. But I assure you there is a richness gained from using so many eyes. Most people have to get along with a single pair, poor things."

Dan was not only touched, but found he was talking to a woman of taste and insight. He told her a little about the beginnings of his statue, then proceeded to give her what he saw before him, detail by detail.

"You are looking at a figure of a sturdy young man of twenty-one. He has been plowing, but now his back is turned to the plow. His left hand rests a moment on the handle which he is abandoning, perhaps forever. He has flung his long coat across the brace of the plow. His right hand grasps the old-fashioned flintlock musket. His weight is chiefly on his left foot, the right is leaving the ground behind in his first step towards freedom. His whole attitude indicates a pause, as if to listen, before starting off.

"He is dressed in the costume of the Continental—a long waistcoat, caught by one button, with the shirt hitched up loosely at the waist for working, and the sleeves rolled carelessly above the elbow. His breeches disappear into the buttoned leggings—which they called galligaskins—and there are stout cowhide boots. A powder-horn with a pine stopple hangs by a strap over his left shoulder, like a scarf of decoration. His soft hat is cocked a bit to one side with the right brim curled up a little.

"This farmer-soldier's face is thorough-going Yankee, open, strong, a face common to no other country or any other part of this one. His features express the energy and self-command that this young pioneer must have had. I hope they convey some of the ready shrewdness and air of freedom that faces in New England must have had and still have to some extent.

"My man is all man. His frame is stalwart, with the shoulders squarely held at just this side of cockiness. After all, what he was doing was a brash venture, a great venture. I have him at his most alert. The muscles of his bared forearms are tense and unencumbered by flabby flesh, with the full veins showing, even to being a little knotted on his strenuous hands. In short I've tried to make this first democrat alive from head to foot. I hope you can see him now, a man of liberty at the moment of determination, ready to launch into the vigorous action of his first day as a soldier."

"Indeed I can," said the old lady. "You almost make me wish I were in his boots."

The blind visitor asked a few questions about the light and shadow of the statue and then left, unmistakably impressed. Dan sat down. Somehow he felt that he had rounded out his work. It *told*.

19

THE COMPLETED Minute Man was too large to be cast as a unit. So on the morning after the reception, Dan began to take his statue apart. In the intricate procedure of plaster-casting, Roman joints are fashioned so that an arm, to be removed at the shoulder, has a projection that fits into a socket. The same with the other arm, the legs, the head.

Disassembling the work felt, to Dan, a little like cutting out his own heart. He knew the emotions a farmer-soldier had once experienced: they both had launched out into the unknown. Opportunity had roused each of them from boyhood occupations, and irresistible determination had brought them to successful conclusions.

His own mood now was one of gratitude—for the success of his work, and for the surcease from the days and months of prolonged tension. It had been six years since he and Lucy had had their argument down there at the old North Bridge, and he had gone home to prove to her that a minute man could be as commemorative a figure of the Fight as a general on horseback. Six years is a long span in a young man's life.

His relief was not complete, however, for the Ames Foundry might spoil his model. And the site was yet to be chosen. Dan secretly feared that this second fight at the North Bridge, in which his figure was involved, might not turn out as happily for the second Minute Man as it did for the first. The town of Concord had slowly wakened up to what was going on, but now many Concordians had seen the statue in the making, and the studio reception had spread the enthusiasm. Now they wanted the Minute Man placed where all could see. Why poke him up there on Buttrick's Hill? Nobody would see the statue there. For the same reason why hide it down at the Bridge? Half the year nobody bothered to trudge to the Bridge; they had enough snow to contend with at home. Put it on the Mill Dam, or in front of the Library, or on the Square. The Square was the place for it. You approached it from four different roads. Everybody could see it then. It was absurd to bury it in a meadow.

Dan discovered that he possessed fighting blood. This was his statue. Where it stood was almost as important as the figure itself. In this he could not afford to be overruled. Already he had influenced Congress, he told himself, through Judge Hoar, and got enough cannon given to Concord to make the statue cost-free. Why shouldn't they listen to him? But they refused to do so. The idea of isolating the statue in a marsh when it could be proudly exhibited in the heart of the town was crazy . . . crazy . . . crazy.

"It won't be a marsh when it's filled in," Dan said.

"One more plaguey expense!"

Dan had listened to his father talk law cases, business, politics, and had been surprised how many times the tide had been turned by one man, one nuisance of a man who never stopped pushing until the tide thought better of it and began to flow the other way.

166

Dan went again to the Bridge. Even that was discouraging. The new bridge just authorized was way behind schedule. Here it was mid-August and they were only driving the piles. Dan spotted John Keyes with his brother on the bank and rowed over to them. They were poring over the plan of the new bridge.

Dan knew his opportunity. He asked his distinguished relatives to get into his boat. "I want to show you something," he said.

Dan had won George Keyes' respect. No one, thought George Keyes, supposedly the victim of the artistic temperament had been less trouble. No young man had ever conducted himself more modestly or more ably in the prosecution of a big work—not in all of Mr. Keyes' experience. Indeed, nobody was contributing so much as Dan to the success of the now all-important Centennial. He had earned the right to be listened to. So both the Keyes got into the rowboat and let Dan pull them up the stream.

Then Dan turned the boat and rested on his oars. "I want you both to see what I see," he said quietly. "The bridge is finished. Where does it go? Nowhere. Mr. Buttrick has given us only the land needed to make a pleasing garden at the far end. As you come down the new lane to the bridge, what do you see? Nothing. Now my idea is to raise the land there at the far end of the bridge, not only that the garden may be safe from flood and in full view, but safe for the Minute Man. I'd have him backgrounded by a hedge. There he'll stand, looking across the bridge in the direction of his duty—and destiny."

"Well, I never thought of that," said the Chairman of the Committee.

"The site of a statue is part of the statue, Mr. Keyes," Dan said earnestly. "The Minute Man means more here than he would mean on the Mill Dam. Here he's the symbol of

the very thing we're celebrating. People object that they'll
have to come here's to see him. What of it? They have to go
to Paris to see Napoleon's tomb."

"That's right," Mr. Keyes said. "And appreciate it more
for the trouble."

"The truth is that a statue you see day in day out is soon
not seen at all. Here my Minute Man will be fresh, always."

They were impressed, but Dan had them look at the site
from every point of view. They were interrupted by Mr.
Sanborn accompanied by a stranger.

"Gentlemen, allow me to present Mr. Charles Dudley
Warner, the writer. He has just been locating the site for
Mr. Ward's statue of Putnam, and I've brought him here
to see if he doesn't prefer this site for the Minute Man to
any other."

Mr. Warner agreed.

"This is where the Minute Man is to stand," said the
Chairman of the Monument Committee. "The town will
have to like it. Mr. French has convinced me that this is
the most dignified and appropriate place of all."

Dan walked home jubilant. He felt free. The work of
his hands had found its proper resting place there by the
river and the trees and the meadows. It was almost miracu-
lous how things came about—if you knew what you wanted
and kept after it.

When Dan reached home he found visitors, Preston
Powers, a boyhood friend who also had become a sculptor,
and his wife, a charming-looking girl of twenty. This was
precisely the way to celebrate his own fine feeling, Dan
thought.

It was the happiest of reunions. The Powers were on their
way back to Italy, where they lived in a large villa. For
neighbors they had another sculptor, Thomas Ball and his

168

family. Preston made Dan envious by telling him of Mr. Ball's studio and models, and of prices far below the lowest in America. Dan, in turn, informed him wryly of his cavern in the Studio Building in Boston, and the rent he was forced to pay for it.

"You'll have to come to Italy," Powers said. "We have a wonderful place for almost nothing—bowers of roses, orange groves and lemons, with magnificent views of the Arno valley and Florence at our feet."

"It really is ridiculous," chimed in Mrs. Powers. "A handsome villa, a gorgeous walled garden, and all the service in the world for less than you could rent a small house in Boston, and miles of art galleries handy."

"And when you want to relax, you relax in somebody's palace," Preston laughed. "The Palace of the Demidoffs would open your eyes. And a masked ball at the Borghese Palace is like something in a dream—fountains, flowers, music, princesses, flocks of princesses."

"My ideas of Europe have been rather limited, I see," Dan smiled. "Mr. Emerson didn't report any princesses."

"You're not married yet?" Preston asked.

"In this country one has to support a wife," Dan said.

"That settles it!" Preston slapped his knee. "Come to Italy and pick out a princess."

"My husband has some beautiful sisters, too," Mrs. Powers added delightfully.

"Really, Dan, I mean this," Preston said. "Thomas Ball has a huge studio and he'd lend you a corner of it. He has a couple of rooms for marble cutting. Now you must learn that, you admit."

Dan admitted. A strange disturbance was taking place inside of him. Preston was evidently in earnest, and what an opportunity! Italy, Rome, Michelangelo! And of course he wouldn't refuse to speak to a princess if he saw one. It was as if he had been lassoed and the lariat drawn tight about his throat, so sharply was his breath cut off by these beckoning possibilities.

The talk shifted to the Minute Man and Dan showed photographs of the seven-foot model. The Powers' enthusiasm warmed him further.

"When will your work be through?" Preston asked.

"When the casting's done—a month or so."

"I have it! You come over then and stay with us. And our villa is huge. We don't use half of it. We'll give you a room with a view of the Campanile and Monte Senaria, and then you can come back in April for the unveiling."

"The trouble is that sailing to and fro on the Atlantic Ocean costs money," Dan said ruefully. "And money isn't the thing I have most of. Or anybody, for that matter. We're trying to ride out a panic. It's pretty unpredictable what's going to happen. Hundreds of banks have failed, and thousands of businesses, and I can't ask father for a jaunt to Europe. I'm going to plunge into something that will really pay."

"But surely they pay you handsomely for this glorious Minute Man!" Mrs. Powers exclaimed.

Dan explained. "Concord's done well by me. They gambled on an unknown and I accepted the bargain. Anyway, it'd be no use to ask for money now. Things are too tight."

"I hear the other side of it from Mr. Ball," Preston said. "Vinnie Ream is getting $20,000 for her 'Farragut.' And Brown, H. K. you know, turned down an offer of $40,000 for an equestrian statue. So you see all the country isn't broke."

These immense sums dazzled Dan, fanning his desire to spread his wings. But it was unthinkable that he should leave before the unveiling. The Powers rose.

"You'll stay to supper, of course!" Dan insisted. "Mother will be home with father and would hate to miss you."

"I'm afraid we can't," Preston said. "We have to be in town by six and we want to pay two or three calls while we're here. We're sailing Saturday."

"Saturday," Dan repeated gauntly. It meant that he had three days to make up his mind as to whether or not they could expect him.

"You know where to reach me, the old address," Preston said. "If you decide to come, you'd better see me before we sail. I can tell you what to bring and how to get to us."

"Please say yes, Mr. French," Mrs. Powers begged.

"I'll say something," Dan smiled, "before you sail. And I can say now it's the finest invitation a fellow ever had to worry over. I can't thank you enough for it."

Dan wandered out into the orchard and down towards the river. He must, he saw plainly, make his decision now. He was not going to let Pamela make it, or Sallie, or even his father. He must not even mention it until he had decided. He wished he could talk it over with someone without being influenced; but you couldn't. This was one of those crises you had to think through yourself—or let the decision come to you, as Patrick would say.

It was brutally hot, he realized. Clouds were piling up in the west in angry glory. The river was like another sky, mirroring the thunderheads and the infinite reaches of blue between them. It was a good place for an artist to make a decision, surrounded by beauty.

Dan sat down. What did he want most? That was the real question. To become a great sculptor . . . to make a fortune . . . to have a good time as he had always had . . . to marry and settle down?

He wanted them all, that was the trouble. On his way to

171

the Bridge a few hours ago he had been picturing himself at the unveiling of his statue, being congratulated by the President of the United States, being the beau of the great ball, perhaps meeting his fate that night, the most fortunate young man in the country. It would be idiotic to run away from all this. Such fame came only once in a lifetime and how often did it come to a man young enough to enjoy it?

Dan sat up straight. The financial possibilities! He had not thought of them. Fifty thousand people were coming. He would be certain to have offers. Suppose some other town wanted a statue? He could ask $10,000 and get it, and what couldn't he do with that money! Pay back his father for all his board and care. Give Pamela some of the luxuries she coveted. And Sallie. Then he *could* go to Europe, *could* marry. That was the sensible answer.

Dan rose. The thunderheads were dragging their violet curtain of rain towards Concord and the windows must be closed. A thunderstorm always excited him. The fury and grandeur and the spice of danger swept his spirits up onto the heights. There was a glorious intensity that thrilled him about these elements gone mad and yet obeying their innate laws. A thunderstorm was a work of art, unhampered by small considerations, overwhelming and gorgeous, yet all contained in the frame of an afternoon. Michelangelo, at his greatest, had something of the same primeval strength. Michelangelo—

Dan stopped in his tracks. Preston was giving him the chance to study Michelangelo. He could sit before those statues for hours remembering the pictures Mr. Emerson had shown him and the words he had uttered about the great master. He heard Mr. Emerson's voice and Dan suddenly felt that his decision by the river might not be final. Mr. Emerson had certainly never fashioned his decisions on the desire for wealth or fame. Yet he was the greatest man in

172

America, greater than Daniel Webster, the traitor in a crisis, greater than President Grant, who was not doing so well in his crisis. Dan knew what Mr. Emerson would counsel—do your work, follow your bent, hitch your wagon to your guiding star, the highest one you can see. It was the same old advice Patrick had given, and he certainly had not re-gretted that. Perhaps this opportunity was as big as the chance to do the Minute Man.

A gust of wind started Dan to the house again. As he went into the familiar rooms to pull down the windows, he felt a sudden emptiness. He would be homesick. It startled him. It meant that somewhere inside him he had decided, hardly consciously, to go to Europe.

"You remember Preston Powers," Dan said almost casually to his father and Pamela at supper. "He and his wife called. They're living in Florence, and they've asked me to come to visit them."

"That would be nice to look forward to sometime," Pamela said.

"Thomas Ball lives there," Dan went on. "I might study with him."

The Judge looked at Dan. There was something pondered in his voice, something he had not put into words.

Pamela finished dishing out the cut peaches, saying, "Do you remember that day in Florence, Henry, when we started to walk to the Uffizi, and you came across all those unfinished drawings and you made that absurd remark?"

"I? I never make an absurd remark, my dear."

"I couldn't drag you away from them and you asked me if I thought it was logically possible to finish looking at an unfinished drawing."

Their laughs were interrupted by Sallie's arrival. "You all look very happy," she said. "I've the grandest news! The

173

program for the celebration's all arranged. It starts with a dawn salute of 100 guns from Lee's Hill. The 5th Regiment will be here and there's to be a monster parade. Dan, you're to be in the first carriage with Judge Hoar, Mr. Emerson, and Mr. Curtis. Can you imagine!" Sallie laughed excitedly. *"We've* got to stand and bow while our little brother rides by! You'll have to start in right now, Dan, practicing to look haughty."

They laughed at the picture of Dan trying to be haughty.

"That's just the start!" Sallie went on. "You leave the carriage, Dan, at the end of the little lane and walk down to your statue. Then the band plays something—"

"God Save the Queen," Dan interpolated.

"Well, it doesn't matter, and then Mr. Emerson does the unveiling and makes a speech. Then everybody comes back to the big pavilion to hear Mr. Curtis make his speech. There are going to be bands and bands, even the Marine Band of the United States, because President Grant will be there. I suppose you'll sit beside the President, Dan."

"I doubt it. Not unless he comes to Italy."

"Italy!" Sallie's voice sharpened in surprise. "What's Italy got to do with it?"

"Dan's been invited to stay with a posse of sculptors over there," the Judge said.

"I thought that was for sometime in the future, dear," Pamela said. "I doubt if Italy would be feasible now."

"But you couldn't possibly go before the celebration!" Sallie exclaimed.

"I'm afraid it's now or never," Dan said a bit grimly. He told of the invitation and of its limitless advantages.

Sallie's color was rising. "Why, that would spoil every-thing!" she cried. "Why I never heard of such a thing, not going to the unveiling of your own statue! There'll be fifty thousand people to see it and you."

174

"You're getting me mixed up with the Revolution, Sallie," Dan said. "It's anything but me they're coming for. Some 49,000 odd don't even know my name."

"But they will, if you stay. You can't go! You *can't!*" Tears were coming.

Dan put his arm about Sallie. "Do you think I haven't considered both sides? If I stay what happens? I hear my statue praised. I hear myself praised. I have to say 'thank you, thank you' all day long like a mechanical doll. I shake hands with the President. I dance till morning. Then I wake up and say 'what next?' But if I go to Italy now I'll be six months ahead. I'll be getting ready to take advantage of any reputation I gain from the Centennial. And it seems to me that that's worth more to me in the long run than hanging around here to be praised and just to have a good time."

Sallie stared. "I don't believe you realize—this is the biggest, the very most important event in your whole life, and you miss it! Father, won't you say something?"

"Yes, but you won't like it. I think Dan is right, absolutely right, and he makes me prouder of him than ever. Don't you, Pamela?"

"I'd have to know more about what he's getting into," said practical Pamela. "Is Preston Powers a good influence, Dan?"

"Not as good as Michelangelo," Dan said with a smile. "But it's not Preston I'm going to study. I think you'll approve of everything, Mother Pamela."

"I never saw such a man!" Sallie said. "He becomes great and then—"

"Greater," the Judge said.

"Perhaps I should retire!" Dan suggested. "This is getting pretty hot."

"I'm through," the Judge said. "But I want Sallie to understand that nothing is more shortsighted than to try to stop a man from being his better self. Now, if you want to cool off, Dan, I wish you'd pick up the windfalls under that early apple before the worms get at them. Then we'll hear more about this."

When Dan approached the kitchen with his green apples he heard voices.

"But it isn't only the celebration!" Sallie was saying. "I can't bear having him so far away. And he won't come back the same nice unspoiled boy he is now."

"He's a man now. His decision shows that," Pamela said, not over-sympathetically. "What is manhood if it isn't the ability to decide, to take life into your own hands, and acknowledge responsibility?"

"You know I don't mean that," Sallie said. "It's temptation. Europe is a terribly immoral place."

"What place isn't if you want it to be?" Pamela exclaimed. "Don't you ever let Dan hear that you don't trust him. If he's kept straight so far, as he clearly has, it's because he has determined to. Now wipe your eyes and be proud of him instead of being a drag. It wasn't an easy decision for him to make."

Dan decided that it was not the opportune time to appear in the kitchen, but he was glad that he had overheard. It was a wonderful help to know that Pamela was so proud of him. She was right, too—so far, and he had no notion of acting any differently.

I F DAN had consciously tried to add to the stir of talk
about him, he could have picked no better way than this
decision to sail away from Concord and miss the unveiling
of his statue.

The news hit its hearers with forceful impact. A few were
shocked to think that anything so irregular could ever be
thought of, for by now the Centennial Celebration loomed
so high that it filled the whole horizon. Leaving for Europe
in the face of its glory was almost an act of levity.

Others were different. They quickly congratulated Dan,
for a trip to Europe in 1874 was an enviable experience.
They thought Dan was a lucky fellow to go, and they didn't
blame him for doing so. There was something adventurous
about it that caught their imaginations, like eloping with
an heiress. These people were all smiles and full of good
wishes.

A third group saw deeper. Families like the Emersons and
Alcotts and Keyes and Bartletts and the girls who knew Dan
best understood the quality of Dan's decision. Their imaginations ran sensitively to his point of view and compre-

hended his struggle. The expressions of their admiration were quiet but full of a fine emotion. Dan warmed to their appreciation of him, and for their sakes Concord became dearer than ever.

When he went to procure a reservation on the *Atlas* sailing from Boston on October 19, his father went with him. The Judge had been abroad more than once and knew how to size up a vessel. "She's a nice clean ship," he said to his son. "I envy you your first crossing, Dan. It's like discovering a new world."

"I solemnly retract every joke I've made about seasickness," Dan said with a smile.

"You'll be too interested to be sick. I never was."

September passed in a rush of parties and preparations. The fall was always Concord's most joyous season. Winter's magnificence was too cold to be appreciated; spring was a pitiful tease; summer overdid itself; but fall was an exultation of crisp mornings, blue skies, and warm afternoons. Chestnut hunting took the place of swimming. Steak-roasts on Egg Rock were not disturbed by mosquitoes, and the leaves said goodbye in a wave of color day after day.

"Goodbye" was not only on nature's lips, it was in Dan's heart. He went to Chicopee to pay a farewell visit to the Minute Man and found that the Ames people had made a perfect job of casting his statue.

Dan took one last look at this work that represented so much of himself. It was good, his inner conscience told him —that artist conscience that he had never taught to lie. This figure was a part of himself; it had stepped out of his mind for the world to see, and he was not ashamed of it. No money, no fame would have made up for this other thing, this approbation of his conscience. Now he could let the statue rest and go on to something else.

His eyes caught the inscription in the bronze:

D. C. French fecit

Concord 1874

He could look at those words impersonally now. At the best they were only part of the truth. His father had helped make that statue when he brought home that first lump of clay. And Pamela, when she had lectured him on the Dolly Varden sentimentality, had contributed her bit. And Mr. Ward, and Patrick, and the unseen force that had flowed through him all these years directing his hand, his heart, his mind. When you thought of all these influences on your work there was small chance of being an egotist.

The workmen had left Dan alone amid the clutter and cranes of the shop and he turned away thankful he had elected to go abroad. In his mind's eye he saw the flags dropping from the Minute Man as Mr. Emerson pulled the cord, heard the first murmurs of the crowd as they gazed on the statue. He saw now that all this was nothing to miss, or almost nothing. The moment for enjoyment of your work was while you were doing it.

The last parties for Dan came in clusters, like the south-moving birds. He was practically public property now. Mr. and Mrs. Emerson tendered him a farewell supper. Sallie and Ned had a party for him in their home. Beth Hoar gave an elaborate dance. His father and Pamela staged a reception, and Will Brewster came to make merry with Richard Dana.

At last came time for packing, then the last night at home, the last breakfast, the trip to the station. The family were going in to Boston to see him off, but Patrick wasn't. Dan shook that horny hand and said, "See what you got me into, Patrick, with your encouragement. But for you I might be staying here in peace and quiet and growing radishes."

179

"Faith, and I almost wish I'd held my tongue," Patrick said. "Where do you go first?"

"Liverpool, then London, then Paris and down the length of France and so on to Florence, and my friend will meet me at the station."

"Well, I hope for your sake the ocean has changed its nature since I was on it," Patrick said. "Good luck to you, whatever comes."

Indian summer had never provided a lovelier afternoon for the start of a journey—all golden warmth and soft distances —but conversation lagged. The human race had not discovered an easy way of parting from those it loved. The family went aboard to inspect Dan's stateroom; to Dan, the *Atlas* already felt like home.

"Reassuring name, *Atlas*," Dan said, determined not to let the occasion grow solemn. "Ought to keep me afloat anyway."

"I just hate to think of you alone on the Atlantic Ocean," Sallie said.

Dan laughed. "The captain has promised to go, too, Sallie. And I don't suppose *all* the crew will be washed overboard."

"You know what I mean. Suppose you get sick?"

"If I lived through these last weeks, I'm indestructible."

Sallie smiled wanly and said, "In any case I brought you this, Dan," and she presented him with a beautiful little compass. "May it guide you safely to your goal."

"Did you say girl? Or goal?" Dan asked, admiring the compass. "I see you've put their initials on it. N for Nellie . . . E for Elizabeth . . . S for Sallie . . . and W . . . What's W for?"

"W is for West," Pamela said quickly. "The direction you take to come home. And now I think we'll leave you, Dan. Don't let Will Brewster keep you up too late."

"No, we're going to have dinner at the Parker House and

then take in the Marionettes. You don't have to worry about my sleeping, Mother Pamela."

They kissed him goodbye, while Sallie wiped her eyes surreptitiously, and Dan's throat went tight and his mouth set. . . . And then they were gone.

But not quite. For when Will Brewster brought him back to the *Atlas* at midnight, and Dan had lighted the little lamp in his stateroom, he saw an envelope on his pillow with his father's handwriting, just as on that night he had turned twenty-one. "To be opened at Sea," it said. He undressed, blew out the lamp, and lay back in his bunk. That letter under the pillow was his father all over, full of forethought and care. It did not have to be opened to be read. He was infinitely lucky to have such a father . . . such a friend . . . he must be worthy. . . .

The dark had closed in. Dan slept.

THE LETTERS about the great day in Concord reached Dan in May. In the six months since that first night he had gone to bed at sea, he had been living in a dream world. The Powers, the Ball family, and all the Italians, titled or untitled, who liked Dan at sight and accepted him as one of them, had made a paradise of his days and nights.

Add Florence, add Italy, add the excitement of the strange and the beautiful everywhere, a grand studio to work in, rich and unusual food, a tricky climate for all its cajoling surface, and the thing his home folks dreaded happened. Dan tired himself out and was sick.

He hated himself for it. He always had resented any slight ailment. It was like a sin. The ladies did not treat him as a sinner, however, but as a fellow-American far from home who needed mothering. And when he was on his feet again, Mr. and Mrs. Ball took him on a leisurely trip to Rome and Naples.

On that April 19th which was never quite absent from his thoughts, Dan climbed Mount Vesuvius. He hoped it was as beautiful a day at home and that there had been no hitch in the unveiling of his statue. From then on he was a little taut, very eager for the news.

At last it came in a flood. His family was as intelligent as ever in reporting the Day. Each told what he or she saw, letting the sum of their individual impressions and emotions build a complete picture for the absent hero of it all. As he read the closely-written pages, he heard the town wakened by the artillery, felt the disappointment when the brilliant day clouded over with a freezing wind. He saw the military forming along the road in front of his home—two miles of soldiers punctuated with bands. He saw his father riding as his deputy in that first carriage laden with celebrities, escorted by the Sixth Regiment.

They described Mr. Emerson's calm thrilling voice dedicating his statue and Dan was moved with pride at the engraving of the first stanza of the Concord Hymn on the statue's base. That was something to think about—Emerson and Dan French coupled for all time, the young hopeful and the immortal. Did that make him immortal too? He re-read Miss Preston's letter:

Such a sweet illumination came, just as the veil of American flags dropped from the statue and the splendid creature leaped forth in the fullness of his life and vigor—your first great work, Dan, as it is now simple justice to call it—yes, it is much greater than I thought. The intense vitality, the invincible manhood of the creature which used to impress, I might almost say oppress, me so much when I saw it in the clay, seem now to have found their true atmosphere. They transcend all technical merit and command the homage of all who see. Mr. Curtis used the right word, it is *masterly*. And he said what we all feel only too keenly when he added that we hardly know what to hope of one who has done so mature a work before reaching 25. And Mrs. Forbes, Mr. Emerson's beautiful daughter said, "I remember well the celebration of 25 years ago, and I don't see how the last quarter of a century could have begun more gloriously than with the birth of your son." (This was to your Father and Mother at the Ball.) It was good to watch him when all this homage was paid him on your behalf, and I know it will be good for you to hear of his joy.

Dan was moved. Surely he must accomplish more, must be worth this praise and their faith in him. He read Pamela's fine letter, and Sallie's outcry of fondness and excitement, and Will's conscientious effort to make him participate in the day's history.

The only drawback had been the piercing cold. Will reported many of the jokes people had made at their discomfort. The Judge had feared there would be more casualties from pneumonia than both sides had suffered in the Fight. And Will said they repeated the words that a hundred years before Major Buttrick had addressed to his troops (and with even greater earnestness), "For God's sake, *fire!*"

He came back to his father's letter and read certain parts over again:

The Minute Man is triumphant. Everybody admires, nobody finds any fault. The amateur and the laborer agree that it is fine. I attended the Ball till 2 a.m. and most of my time was occupied in receiving congratulations on your success, and I confess to some pride. Mr. Blaine said that it seemed as if the whole Centennial was got up to glorify you. The Rev. Mr. Reynolds mentioned you in his sermon, preached from a text in II Samuel, 22:23 "God is my strength and power: and he maketh my way perfect." The sum of all our thoughts is "God bless the boy."

184

Dan sat still with the letters strewn about him. This was, they all said it, fame. This was how it felt to be famous—thankful, happy, tender, stimulated, and very, very grateful. The sunset was filling the valley of the Arno with light of gold. Soon the towers of the storied city beneath him would be dim, but over his country the light was still bright.

It had been a temptation to accept Mr. Ball's invitation and settle down in Italy. Lucy's letter announcing her engagement had disturbed him a bit, though he knew that he had never had a real desire to marry her. He had not met the right girl yet, but he would, and she would be no dark and titled Italian, but an American, who loved views of high hills and sparkling air. He had passed this temptation, too, this seduction of Europe. He would go back and absorb the clean strength of America into his work as he had begun to do in the Minute Man.

The sky was now a faint celestial blue, a ceiling by Raphael, and he saw the sharp curve of the new moon. Sallie would be seeing it in a few hours, and Sallie had told him that she would always think of her baby brother when she saw the moon. Sallie was sentimental but she was very comforting when you were three thousand miles from home. They were all wonderful, all his family. These letters had lifted him up. He felt like work again. He'd show them now what he could really do!

1775

NINETEENTH
OF
APRIL

1875